Isaac Asimov has been one of the most prolific and widely read authors in the field of popular science for the last twenty years. Over a hundred of his books have been published, ranging from science fiction and pure science to history, religion and geography. His work is received with equal enthusiasm by sf fans, academics and students. Dr. Asimov currently lives in New York City, devoting the greater part of his time to writing.

*Also by Isaac Asimov and available
from Sphere Books*

PEBBLE IN THE SKY
A WHIFF OF DEATH
THE BEST OF ISAAC ASIMOV
THE HUGO WINNERS Books 1 and 2 (Ed.)
WHERE DO WE GO FROM HERE? Book 2 (Ed.)

Where Do We Go From Here?

Book 1

Edited by ISAAC ASIMOV

SPHERE BOOKS LIMITED
30/32 Gray's Inn Road, London WC1X 8JL

First published in Great Britain
by Michael Joseph Limited 1973
Copyright © Isaac Asimov 1971
Published by Sphere Books (in two volumes) 1974

Dedication

To Judy-Lynn Benjamin who is full of surprises,
birthday and otherwise

Set in Linotype Baskerville

Printed in Great Britain by
Hazell Watson & Viney Ltd
Aylesbury, Bucks

ISBN 0 7221 1251 3

Publisher's Note

In order to produce this excellent collection at a reasonable length and price, it was necessary to divide the original publication into two books. Isaac Asimov's introduction and the appendix are printed in both.

Grateful acknowledgement is made to the following for permission to reprint the articles included in this book:

'Surface Tension' by James Blish, first published in *Galaxy Magazine*, August 1952. Copyright © 1957 by James Blish. Reprinted by permission of the author and Robert P. Mills, Ltd.;

'The Day Is Done' by Lester del Rey, first published in *Astounding Science Fiction*, May 1939. Copyright 1939 by Street & Smith Publications, Inc. Reprinted by permission of the author and his agents, Scott Meredith Literary Agency Inc.;

'A Subway Named Mobius' by A. J. Deutsch, first published in *Astounding Science Fiction*, December 1950. Copyright 1950 by Street & Smith Publications, Inc.;

'Heavy Planet' by Milton A. Rothman, first published under the name of Lee Gregor, in *Astounding Science Fiction*, August 1939. Copyright 1939 by Street & Smith Publications, Inc. Reprinted by permission of the author;

'—And He Built a Crooked House—' by Robert A. Heinlein, first published in *Astounding Science Fiction*, February 1941. Copyright 1940 by Street & Smith Publications, Inc. Reprinted by permission of the author's agents Lurton Blassingame;

'Night' by Don A. Stuart, first published in *Astounding Stories*, October 1935. Copyright © 1935 by Street & Smith Publications, Inc. Copyright © renewed 1963 by the Condé Nast Publications, Inc. Reprinted by permission of the author and his agents, Scott Meredith Literary Agency, Inc.;

'A Martian Odyssey' by Stanley G. Weinbaum, first published in *Wonder Stories*, July 1934. Copyright 1934 by Continental Publications, Inc.; Copyright renewed 1962 by Margaret Weinbaum Kay. Published by arrangement with Forrest J. Ackerman representing the author's estate.

CONTENTS

INTRODUCTION

I have long maintained that science fiction has potential as an inspiring and useful teaching device. For this anthology, therefore, I have selected seventeen stories which, I think, can inspire curiosity and can lead the student into lines of questioning of his own that may interest and excite him, and may even help determine the future direction of his career.

This is not to say that the stories are all scientifically accurate though some, of course, are indeed accurate by the standards of their times. After all, a science fiction story cannot be (except by inspired guessing) more accurate than the scientific knowledge of the time makes possible. A story written in 1925 can only by accident deal accurately with Pluto, the ninth planet; and the situation is similar in stories about the atomic bomb written in 1935; artificial satellites written in 1945; quasars written in 1955, and so on.

In many science fiction stories, a scientific principle is deliberately bent for the sake of making a particular plot possible. This can be done skilfully by an author knowledgeable in science or clumsily by another who is less well versed in the matter. In either case, even in the latter, the story can be useful. A law of nature ignored or distorted can rouse more interest, sometimes, than a law of nature explained. Are the events in the story possible? If not, why not? And in tracking that down, the student may sometimes learn more about science than from any number of correct classroom demonstrations.

This anthology is prepared, then, on several different levels.

In the first place, the seventeen stories included are all good ones, all clever and exciting in their own right. Anyone who wishes can read them for themselves alone, need make no conscious effort to learn from them, and may totally ignore my own comments after each story.

For those who would probe a little deeper, I have placed after each story a few hundred words of commentary in which I talk about the scientific points made in the story, pointing out their validity or, sometimes, explaining their errors.

Finally, after each comment, I have appended a series of suggestions and questions designed to direct the reader's curiosity in possibly fruitful directions. These are not simple, nor are they intended to be simple; sometimes indeed I ask questions that have no known answers. Nevertheless, I give no hints and there are no answers in the back of the book. I have, however, in an appendix at the end of the book, listed two items for each story that might interest anyone who found himself gripped by the science involved. The further reading may not give the answers to the questions I posed but they will answer other questions which I did not ask and they will very likely lure the reader onward.

Even this appendix, rough and non-specific though it is, I present reluctantly. I want the reader completely on his own. I don't want to give answers but to stimulate thought; I don't want to point out solutions but to rouse the kind of curiosity that may begin a self-directed drive.

There is, after all, no requirement that any reader follow up all or even any of the lines of inquiry I suggest, but a few might, out of a desire nurtured by the stories in this anthology, or even by just one particular story.

If that happens, then for each reader that finds even one thread of suggestion exciting and proceeds to lose himself in the search for knowledge, I win immensely more than I would have won by merely providing an interesting anthology.

And the involved readers win immensely more as well.

I. A MARTIAN ODYSSEY

Stanley G. Weinbaum

Jarvis stretched himself as luxuriously as he could in the cramped general quarters of the *Ares*.

'Air you can breathe!' he exulted. 'It feels as thick as soup after the thin stuff out there!' He nodded at the Martian landscape stretching flat and desolate in the light of the nearer moon, beyond the glass of the port.

The other three stared at him sympathetically – Putz, the engineer, Leroy, the biologist, and Harrison the astronomer and captain of the expedition. Dick Jarvis, of course, was chemist of the famous crew, the *Ares* expedition, first human beings to set foot on the mysterious neighbour of the earth, the planet Mars. This, of course, was in the old days, less than twenty years after the mad American Doheny perfected the atomic blast at the cost of his life, and only a decade after the equally mad Cardoza rode on it to the moon. They were true pioneers, these four of the *Ares*. Except for a half-dozen moon expeditions and the ill-fated de Lancey flight aimed at the seductive orb of Venus, they were the first men to feel other gravity than earth's, and certainly the first successful crew to leave the earth-moon system. And they deserved that success when one considers the difficulties and discomforts – the months spent in acclimatization chambers back on earth, learning to breathe air as tenuous as that of Mars, the challenging of the void in the tiny rocket driven by the cranky reaction motors of the twenty-first century, and mostly the facing of an absolutely unknown world.

Jarvis stretched again and fingered the raw and peeling tip of his frost-bitten nose. He sighed again contentedly.

'Well,' exploded Harrison abruptly, 'are we going to hear what happened? You set out all shipshape in an auxiliary rocket, we don't get a peep for ten days, and finally Putz here picks you out of a lunatic ant-heap with a freak ostrich as your pal! Spill it, man!'

' "Speel"?' queried Leroy perplexedly. 'Speel what?'

'He means "*spiel*",' explained Putz soberly. 'It iss to tell.'

Jarvis met Harrison's amused glance without the shadow of a smile. 'That's right, Karl,' he said in grave agreement with Putz. '*Ich spiel es!*' He grunted comfortably and began.

'According to orders,' he said, 'I watched Karl here take off towards the North, and then I got into my flying sweat-box and headed South. You'll remember, Cap – we had orders not to land, but just scout about for points of interest. I set the two cameras clicking and buzzed along, riding pretty high – about two thousand feet – for a couple of reasons. First, it gave the cameras a greater field, and second, the under-jets travel so far in this half-vacuum they call air here that they stir up dust if you move low.'

'We know all that from Putz,' grunted Harrison. 'I wish you'd saved the films, though. They'd have paid the cost of this junket; remember how the public mobbed the first moon pictures?'

'The films are safe,' retorted Jarvis. 'Well,' he resumed, 'as I said, I buzzed along at a pretty good clip; just as we figured, the wings haven't much lift in this air at less than a hundred miles per hour, and even then I had to use the under-jets.

'So, with the speed and the altitude and the blurring caused by the under-jets, the seeing wasn't any too good. I could see enough, though, to distinguish that what I sailed over was just more of this grey plain that we'd been examining the whole week since our landing – same blobby growths and same eternal carpet of crawling little plant-animals, or biopods, as Leroy calls them. So I sailed along, calling back my position every hour as instructed, and not knowing whether you heard me.'

'I did?' snapped Harrison.

'A hundred and fifty miles south,' continued Jarvis imperturbably, 'the surface changed to a sort of low plateau, nothing but desert and orange-tinted sand. I figured that we were right in our guess, then, and this grey plain we dropped on was really the Mare Cimmerium which would make my orange desert the region called Xanthus. If I were right, I ought to hit another grey plain, the Mare Chronium in another couple of hundred miles, and then another orange desert, Thyle I or II. And so I did.'

'Putz verified our position a week and a half ago!' grumbled the Captain. 'Let's get to the point.'

'Coming!' remarked Jarvis. 'Twenty miles into Thyle – believe it or not – I crossed a canal!'

'Putz photographed a hundred! Let's hear something new!'

'And did he also see a city?'

'Twenty of 'em, if you call those heaps of mud cities!'

'Well,' observed Jarvis, 'from here on I'll be telling a few things Putz didn't see!' He rubbed his tingling nose, and continued. 'I knew that I had sixteen hours of daylight at this season, so eight hours – eight hundred miles – from here, I decided to turn back. I was still over Thyle, whether I or II I'm not sure, not more than twenty-five miles into it. And right there, Putz's pet motor quit!'

'Quit? How?' Putz was solicitous.

'The atomic blast got weak. I started losing altitude right away, and suddenly there I was with a thump right in the middle of Thyle! Smashed my nose on the window, too!' He rubbed the injured member ruefully.

'Did you maybe try vashing der combustion chamber mit acid sulphuric?' inquired Putz. 'Sometimes der lead giffs a secondary radiation—'

'Naw!' said Jarvis disgustedly. 'I wouldn't try that, of course – not more than ten times! Besides, the bump flattened the landing gear and busted off the under-jets. Suppose I got the thing working – what then? Ten miles with the blast coming right out of the bottom and I'd have melted the floor from under me!' He rubbed his nose again. 'Lucky for me a pound only weighs seven ounces here, or I'd have been mashed flat!'

'I could have fixed!' ejaculated the engineer. 'I bet it vas not serious.'

'Probably not,' agreed Jarvis sarcastically. 'Only it wouldn't fly. Nothing serious, but I had my choice of waiting to be picked up or trying to walk back – eight hundred miles, and perhaps twenty days before we had to leave! Forty miles a day! Well,' he concluded, 'I chose to walk. Just as much chance of being picked up, and it kept me busy.'

'We'd have found you,' said Harrison.

'No doubt. Anyway, I rigged up a harness from some seat straps, and put the water tank on my back, took a cartridge belt and revolver, and some iron rations, and started out.'

'Water tank!' exclaimed the little biologist, Leroy. 'She weigh one-quarter ton!'

'Wasn't full. Weighed about two hundred and fifty pounds earth-weight, which is eighty-five here. Then, besides, my own personal two hundred and ten pounds is only seventy on Mars, so, tank and all, I grossed a hundred and fifty-five, or fifty-five pounds less than my everyday earth-weight. I figured on that when I undertook the forty-mile daily stroll. Oh – of course, I took a thermo-skin sleeping bag for these wintry Martian nights.'

'Off I went, bouncing along pretty quickly. Eight hours of daylight meant twenty miles or more. It got tiresome, of course – plugging along over a soft sand desert with nothing to see, not even Leroy's crawling biopods. But an hour or so brought me to the canal – just a dry ditch about four hundred feet wide, and straight as a railroad on its own company map.

'There'd been water in it sometime, though. The ditch was covered with what looked like a nice green lawn. Only, as I approached, the lawn moved out of my way!'

'Eh?' said Leroy.

'Yeah; it was a relative of your biopods. I caught one – a little grass-like blade about as long as my finger, with two thin, stemmy legs.'

'He is where?' Leroy was eager.

'He is let go! I had to move, so I ploughed along with the walking grass opening in front and closing behind. And then I was out on the orange desert of Thyle again.

'I plugged doggedly along, cussing the sand that made going so tiresome, and, incidentally, cussing that cranky motor of yours, Karl. It was just before twilight that I reached the edge of Thyle, and looked down over the grey Mare Chronium. And I knew there was seventy-five miles of *that* to be walked over, and then a couple of hundred miles of that Xanthus desert, and about as much more Mare Cimmerium. Was I pleased? I started cussing you fellows for not picking me up!'

'We were trying, you sap!' said Harrison.

'That didn't help. Well, I figured I might as well use what was left of daylight in getting down the cliff that

14

bounded Thyle. I found an easy place, and down I went. Mare Chronium was just the same sort of place as this – crazy leafless plants and a bunch of crawlers; I gave it a glance and hauled out my sleeping bag. Up to that time, you know, I hadn't seen anything worth worrying about on this half-dead world – nothing dangerous, that is.'

'Did you?' queried Harrison.

'*Did* I! You'll hear about it when I come to it. Well, I was just about to turn in when suddenly I heard the wildest sort of shenanigans!'

'Vot iss shenanigans!' inquired Putz.

'He say, "*Je ne sais quoi*",' explained Leroy. 'It is to say, "I don't know what".'

'That's right,' agreed Jarvis. 'I didn't know what, so I sneaked over to find out. There was a racket like a flock of crows eating a bunch of canaries – whistles, cackles, caws, trills, and what have you. I rounded a clump of stumps, and there was Tweel!'

'Tweel?' said Harrison, and 'Tveel?' said Leroy and Putz.

'That freak ostrich,' explained the narrator. 'At least, Tweel is as near as I can pronounce it without sputtering. He called it something like 'Trrrweerrlll'.'

'What was he doing?' asked the Captain.

'He was being eaten! And squealing, of course, as any one would.'

'Eaten! By what?'

'I found out later. All I could see then was a bunch of black ropy arms tangled around what looked like, as Putz described it to you, an ostrich. I wasn't going to interfere, naturally; if both creatures were dangerous, I'd have one less to worry about.

'But the bird-like thing was putting up a good battle, dealing vicious blows with an eighteen-inch beak, between screeches. And besides, I caught a glimpse or two of what was on the end of those arms!' Jarvis shuddered. 'But the clincher was when I noticed a little black bag or case hung about the neck of the bird-like thing! It was intelligent! That or tame, I assumed. Anyway, it clinched my decision. I pulled out my automatic and fired into what I could see of its antagonist.

'There was a flurry of tentacles and a spurt of black corruption, and then the thing, with a disgusting sucking noise, pulled itself and its arms into a hole in the ground. The other let out a series of clacks, staggered around on legs about as thick as golf sticks, and turned suddenly to face me. I held my weapon ready, and the two of us stared at each other.

'The Martian wasn't a bird, really. It wasn't even bird-like, except just at first glance. It had a beak all right, and a few feathery appendages, but the beak wasn't really a beak. It was somewhat flexible; I could see the tip bend slowly from side to side; it was almost like a cross between a beak and a trunk. It had four-toed feet, and four-fingered things – hands, you'd have to call them, and a little roundish body, and a long neck ending in a tiny head – and that beak. It stood an inch or so taller than I, and – well, Putz saw it!'

The engineer nodded. 'Yah! I saw!'

CHAPTER II

Tweel of Mars

Jarvis continued. 'So – we stared at each other. Finally the creature went into a series of clackings and twitterings and held out its hands towards me, empty. I took that as a gesture of friendship.'

'Perhaps,' suggested Harrison, 'it looked at that nose of yours and thought you were its brother!'

'Huh!' You can be funny without talking! Anyway, I put up my gun and said, "Aw, don't mention it," or something of the sort, and the thing came over and we were pals.

'By that time, the sun was pretty low and I knew that I'd better build a fire or get into my thermo-skin. I decided on the fire. I picked a spot at the base of the Thyle cliff, where the rock could reflect a little heat on my back. I started breaking off chunks of this desiccated Martian vegetation, and my companion caught the idea and brought in an armful. I reached for a match, but the Martian fished into his pouch and brought out something that looked like a glowing coal; one touch of it, and the fire was blazing – and you all know what a job we have starting a fire in this atmosphere!

'And that bag of his!' continued the narrator. 'That was a manufactured article, my friends; press an end and

16

she popped open – press the middle, and she sealed so perfectly you couldn't see the line. Better than zippers.

'Well, we stared at the fire a while and I decided to attempt some sort of communication with the Martian. I pointed at myself and said "Dick"; he caught the drift immediately, stretched a bony claw at me and repeated "Tick". Then I pointed at him, and he gave that whistle I called Tweel; I can't imitate his accent. Things were going smoothly; to emphasize the names, I repeated "Dick", and then, pointing at him, "Tweel".

'There we stuck! He gave some clacks that sounded negative, and said something like "P-p-p-proot". And that was just the beginning; I was always "Tick", but as for him – part of the time he was "Tweel", and part of the time he was "P-p-p-proot", and part of the time he was sixteen other noises!

'We just couldn't connect! I tried "rock", and I tried "star", and "tree", and "fire", and Lord knows what else, and try as I would, I couldn't get a single word! Nothing was the same for two successive minutes, and if that's a language, I'm an alchemist! Finally I gave it up and called him Tweel, and that seemed to do.

'But Tweel hung on to some of my words. He remembered a couple of them, which I suppose is a great achievement if you're used to a language you have to make up as you go along. But I couldn't get the hang of his talk; either I missed some subtle point or we just didn't *think* alike – and I rather believe the latter view.

'I've other reasons for believing that. After a while I gave up the language business, and tried mathematics. I scratched two plus two equals four on the ground, and demonstrated it with pebbles. Again Tweel caught the idea, and informed me that three plus three equals six. Once more we seemed to be getting somewhere.

'So, knowing that Tweel had at least a grammar school education, I drew a circle for the sun, pointing first at it, and then at the last glow of the sun. Then I sketched in Mercury, and Venus, and Mother Earth, and Mars, and finally, pointing to Mars, I swept my hand around in a sort of inclusive gesture to indicate that Mars was our current environment. I was working up to putting over the idea that my home was on the earth.

'Tweel understood my diagram all right. He poked his beak at it, and with a great deal of trilling and clucking, he added Deimos and Phobos to Mars, and then sketched in the earth's moon!

'Do you see what that proves? It proves that Tweel's race uses telescopes – that they're civilized!'

'Does not!' snapped Harrison. 'The moon is visible from here as a fifth magnitude star. They could see its revolution with the naked eye.'

'The moon, yes!' said Jarvis. 'You've missed my point. Mercury isn't visible! And Tweel knew of Mercury because he placed the moon at the *third* planet, not the second. If he didn't know Mercury, he'd put the earth second, and Mars third, instead of fourth? See?'

'Humph!' said Harrison.

'Anyway,' proceeded Jarvis, 'I went on with my lesson. Things were going smoothly, and it looked as if I could put the idea over. I pointed at the earth on my diagram, and then at myself, and then, to clinch it, I pointed to myself and then to the earth itself shining green almost at the zenith.

'Tweel set up such an excited clacking that I was certain he understood. He jumped up and down, and suddenly he pointed at himself and then at the sky, and then at himself and at the sky again. He pointed at his middle and then at Arcturus, at his head and then at Spica, at his feet and then at half a dozen stars, while I just gaped at him. Then, all of a sudden, he gave a tremendous leap. Man, what a hop! He shot straight up into the starlight, seventy-five feet if an inch! I saw him silhouetted against the sky, saw him turn and come down at me head first, and land smack on his beak like a javelin! Then he stuck square in the centre of my sun-circle in the sand – a bull's-eye!'

'Nuts!' observed the Captain. 'Plain nuts!'

'That's what I thought, too! I just stared at him open-mouthed while he pulled his head out of the sand and stood up. Then I figured he'd missed my point, and I went through the whole blamed rigmarole again, and it ended the same way, with Tweel on his nose in the middle of my picture!'

'Maybe it's a religious rite,' suggested Harrison.

'Maybe,' said Jarvis dubiously. 'Well, there we were. We could exchange ideas up to a certain point, and then – blooey! Something in us was different, unrelated; I don't doubt that Tweel thought me just as screwy as I thought him. Our minds simply looked at the world from different viewpoints, and perhaps his viewpoint is as true as ours. But – we couldn't get together, that's all. Yet, in spite of all difficulties, I *liked* Tweel, and I have a queer certainty that he liked me.'

'Nuts!' repeated the Captain. 'Just daffy!'

'Yeah? Wait and see. A couple of times I've thought that perhaps we—' He paused, and then resumed his narrative. 'Anyway, I finally gave it up, and got into my thermo-skin to sleep. The fire hadn't kept me any too warm, but that damn sleeping bag did. Got stuffy five minutes after I closed myself in. I opened it a little and bingo! Some eighty-below-zero air hit my nose, and that's when I got this pleasant little frostbite to add to the bump I acquired during the crash of my rocket.

'I don't know what Tweel made of my sleeping. He sat around, but when I woke up, he was gone. I'd just crawled out of my bag, though, when I heard some twittering, and there he came, sailing down from that three-storey Thyle cliff to alight on his beak beside me. I pointed to myself and towards the north, and he pointed at himself and towards the south, but when I loaded up and started away, he came along.

'Man, how he travelled! – a hundred and fifty feet at a jump, sailing through the air stretched out like a spear, and landing on his beak. He seemed surprised at my plodding, but after a few moments he fell in beside me, only every few minutes he'd go into one of his leaps, and stick his nose into the sand a block ahead of me. Then he'd come shooting back at me; it kept me nervous at first to see that beak of his coming at me like a spear, but he always ended in the sand at my side.

'So the two of us plugged along across the Mare Chronium. Same sort of place as this – same crazy plants and same little green biopods growing in the sand, or crawling out of your way. We talked – not that we understood each other, you know, but just for company. I sang songs, and I suspect Tweel did too; at least, some of his trillings and twitterings had a subtle sort of rhythm.

'Then, for variety, Tweel would display his smattering of English words. He'd point to an outcropping and say "rock", and point to a pebble and say it again; or he'd touch my arm and say "Tick", and then repeat it. He seemed terrifically amused that the same word meant

19

the same thing twice in succession or that the same word could apply to two different objects. It set me wondering if perhaps his language wasn't like the primitive speech of earth people – you know, Captain, like the Negritoes, for instance, who haven't any generic words. No word for food or water or man – words for good food and bad food, or rain water and sea water, or strong man and weak man – but no names for general classes. They're too primitive to understand that rain water and sea water are just different aspects of the same thing. But that wasn't the case with Tweel; it was just that we were somehow mysteriously different – our minds were alien to each other. And yet – we *liked* each other!'

'Looney, that's all,' remarked Harrison. 'That's why you two were so fond of each other.'

'Well, I like *you*!' countered Jarvis wickedly. 'Anyway,' he resumed, 'don't get the idea that there was anything screwy about Tweel. In fact, I'm not so sure but that he couldn't teach our highly praised human intelligence a trick or two. Oh, he wasn't an intellectual superman, I guess; but don't overlook the point that he managed to understand a little of my mental workings, and I never even got a glimmering of his.'

'Because he didn't have any!' suggested the Captain, while Putz and Leroy blinked attentively.

'You can judge of that when I'm through,' said Jarvis. 'Well, we plugged along across the Mare Chronium all that day, and all the next. Mare Chronium – Sea of Time! Say, I was willing to agree with Schiaparelli's name by the end of that march! Just that grey, endless plain of weird plants, and never a sign of any other life. It was so monotonous that I was even glad to see the desert of Xanthus towards the evening of the second day.

'I was fair worn out, but Tweel seemed as fresh as ever, for all I never saw him drink or eat. I think he could have crossed the Mare Chronium in a couple of hours with those block-long nosedives of his, but he stuck along with me. I offered him some water once or twice; he took the cup from me and sucked the liquid into his beak, and then carefully squirted it all back into the cup and gravely returned it.

'Just as we sighted Xanthus, or the cliffs that bounded it, one of those nasty sand clouds blew along, not as bad as the one we had here, but mean to travel against. I pulled the transparent flap of my thermo-skin bag across my face and managed pretty well, and I noticed that Tweel used some feathery appendages growing like a moustache at the base of his beak to cover his nostrils, and some similar fuzz to shield his eyes.'

'He is desert creature!' ejaculated the little biologist, Leroy.

'Huh? Why?'

'He drink no water – he is adapt' for sand storm—'

'Proves nothing! There's not enough water to waste anywhere on this desiccated pill called Mars. We'd call all of it desert on earth, you know.' He paused. 'Anyway, after the sand storm blew over, a little wind kept blowing in our faces, not strong enough to stir the sand. But suddenly things came drifting along from the Xanthus cliffs – small, transparent spheres, for all the world like glass tennis balls! But light – they were almost light enough to float even in this thin air – empty too; at least, I cracked open a couple and nothing came out but a bad smell. I asked Tweel about them, but all he said was "No, no, no", which I took to mean that he knew nothing about them. So they went bouncing by like tumbleweeds, or like soap bubbles, and we plugged on toward Xanthus. Tweel pointed at one of the crystal balls once and said "rock", but I was too tired to argue with him. Later I discovered what he meant.

'We came to the bottom of the Xanthus cliffs finally, when there wasn't much daylight left. I decided to sleep on the plateau if possible; anything dangerous, I reasoned, would be more likely to prowl through the vegetation of the Mare Chronium than the sand of Xanthus. Not that I'd seen a single sign of menace, except the rope-armed black thing that had trapped Tweel, and apparently that didn't prowl at all, but lured its victims within reach. It couldn't lure me while I slept, especially as Tweel didn't seem to sleep at all, but simply sat patiently around all night. I wondered how the creature had managed to trap Tweel, but there wasn't any way of asking him. I found that out too, later; its devilish!

'However, we were ambling around the base of the Xanthus barrier looking for an easy spot to climb. At least, I was. Tweel could have leaped it easily, for the cliffs were lower than Thyle – perhaps sixty feet. I found a place and started up, swearing at the water tank strapped to my back – it didn't bother me except when climbing – and suddenly I heard a sound that I thought I recognized!

'You know how deceptive sounds are in this thin air. A shot sounds like the pop of a cork. But this sound was the drone of a rocket, and sure enough, there went our second auxiliary about ten miles to westward, between me and the sunset!'

'Vas me!' said Putz. 'I hung for you.'

'Yeah; I knew that, but what good did it do me? I hung on to the cliff and yelled and waved with one hand. Tweel saw it too, and set up a trilling and twittering, leaping to the top of the barrier and then high into the air. And while I watched, the machine droned on into the shadows to the south.

'I scrambled to the top of the cliff. Tweel was still pointing and trilling excitedly, shooting up towards the sky and coming down head-on to stick upside down on his beak in the sand. I pointed towards the south and at myself, and he said, "Yes - Yes - Yes"; but somehow I gathered that he thought the flying thing was a relative of mine, probably a parent. Perhaps I did his intellect an injustice; I think now that I did.

'I was bitterly disappointed by the failure to attract attention. I pulled out my thermo-skin bag and crawled into it, as the night chill was already apparent. Tweel stuck his beak into the sand and drew up his legs and arms and looked for all the world like one of those leafless shrubs out there. I think he stayed that way all night.'

'Protective mimicry!' ejaculated Leroy. 'See? He is desert creature!'

CHAPTER III

The Pyramid Being

'In the morning,' resumed Jarvis, 'we started off again. We hadn't gone a hundred yards into Xanthus when I saw something queer! This is one thing Putz didn't photograph, I'll wager!

'There was a line of little pyramids – tiny ones, not more than six inches high, stretching across Xanthus as far as I could see! Little buildings made of pygmy bricks, they were, hollow inside and truncated, or at least broken at the top and empty. I pointed at them and said "What?" to Tweel, but he gave some negative twitters to indicate, I suppose, that he didn't know. So off we went, following the row of pyramids because they ran north, and I was going north.

'Man, we trailed that line for hours! After a while, I noticed another queer thing: they were getting larger. Same number of bricks in each one, but the bricks were larger.

'By noon they were shoulder high. I looked into a couple – all just the same, broken at the top and empty. I examined a brick or two as well; they were silica, and old as creation itself!'

'How you know?' asked Leroy.

'They were weathered – edges rounded. Silica doesn't weather easily even on earth, and in this climate—!'

'How old you think?'

'Fifty thousand – a hundred thousand years. How can I tell? The little ones we saw in the morning were older – perhaps ten times as old. Crumbling. How old would that make *them*? Half a million years? Who knows?' Jarvis paused a moment. 'Well,' he resumed, 'we followed the line. Tweel pointed at them and said "rock" once or twice, but he'd done that many times before. Besides, he was more or less right about these.

'I tried questioning him. I pointed at a pyramid and asked "People?" and indicated the two of us. He set up a negative sort of clucking and said, "No, no, no. No one-one-two. No two-two-four," meanwhile rubbing his stomach. I just stared at him and he went through the business again. "No one-one-two. No two-two-four." I just gaped at him.'

'That proves it!' exclaimed Harrison. 'Nuts!'

'You think so?' queried Jarvis sardonically. 'Well, I figured it out different! "No one-one-two!" You don't get it, of course, do you?'

'Nope – nor do you!'

'I think I do! Tweel was using the few English words he knew to put over a very complex idea. What, let me ask, does mathematics make you think of?'

'Why – of astronomy. Or – of logic!'

'That's it! "No one-one-two!" Tweel was telling me that the builders of the pyramids weren't people! – or that they weren't intelligent, that they weren't reasoning creatures! Get it?'

'Huh! I'll be damned!'

'You probably will.'

'Why,' put in Leroy, 'he rub his belly?'

'Why? Because, my dear biologist, that's where his brains were! Not in his tiny head – in his middle!'

'C'est impossible!'

'Not on Mars, it isn't! This flora and fauna aren't earthly; your biopods prove that!' Jarvis grinned and took up his narrative. 'Anyway, we plugged along across Xanthus and in about the middle of the afternoon, something else queer happened. The pyramids ended.'

'Ended!'

'Yeah; the queer part was that the last one – and now they were ten-footers – was capped! See? Whatever built it was still inside; we'd trailed 'em from their half-million-year-old origin to the present.

'Tweel and I both noticed it about the same time. I yanked out my automatic (I had a clip of Boland explosive bullets in it) and Tweel, quick as a sleight-of-hand trick, snapped a queer little glass revolver out of his bag. It was much like our weapons, except that the grip was larger to accommodate his four-taloned hand. And we held our weapons ready while we sneaked up along the lines of empty pyramids.

'Tweel saw the movement first. The top tiers of bricks were heaving, shaking, and suddenly slid down the sides with a thin crash. And then – something – something was coming out!

'A long, silver-grey arm appeared, dragging after it an armoured body. Armoured, I mean, with scales, silver-grey and dull-shining. The arm heaved the body out of the hole; the beast crashed to the sand.

'It was a nondescript creature – body like a big grey cask, arm and a sort of mouth-hole at one end; stiff, pointed tail at the other – and that's all. No other limbs, no eyes, ears, nose – nothing! The thing dragged itself a few yards, inserted its pointed tail in the sand, pushed itself upright, and just sat.

'Tweel and I watched it for ten minutes before it moved. Then, with a creaking and rustling like – oh, like crumpling stiff paper – its arm moved to the mouth-hole and out came a brick! The arm placed the brick carefully on the ground, and the thing was still again.

'Another ten minutes – another brick. Just one of

Nature's bricklayers. I was about ready to slip away and move on when Tweel pointed at the thing and said "rock"! I went "huh?" and he said it again. Then, to the accompaniment of some of his trilling, he said, "No – no—," and gave two or three whistling breaths.

'Well, I got his meaning, for a wonder! I said, "No breath?" and demonstrated the word. Tweel was ecstatic; he said, "Yes, yes, yes! No, no, no breet!" Then he gave a leap and sailed out to land on his nose about one pace from the monster!

'I was startled, you can imagine! The arm was going up for a brick, and I expected to see Tweel caught and mangled, but – nothing happened! Tweel pounded on the creature, and the arm took the brick and placed it neatly beside the first. Tweel rapped on its body again, and said "rock", and I got up nerve enough to take a look myself.

'Tweel was right again. The creature *was* rock, and it didn't breathe!'

'How you know?' snapped Leroy, his black eyes blazing interest.

'Because I'm a chemist. The beast was made of silica! There must have been pure silicon in the sand, and it lived on that. Get it? We, and Tweel, and those plants out there, and even the biopods are *carbon* life; this thing lived by a different set of chemical reactions. It was silicon life!'

'*La vie silicieuse!*' shouted Leroy. 'I have suspect, and now it is proof! I must go see! *Il faut que je—*'

'All right! All right!' said Jarvis. 'You can go see. Anyhow, there the thing was, alive and not alive, moving every ten minutes, and then only to remove a brick. Those bricks were its waste matter. See, Frenchy? We're carbon, and our waste is carbon dioxide, and this is silicon, and *its* waste is silicon dioxide – silica. But silica is a solid, hence the bricks. And it built itself in, and when it was covered, it moved over to a fresh place to start over. No wonder it creaked! A living creature half a million years old!'

'How you know how old?' Leroy was frantic.

'We trailed its pyramids from the beginning, didn't we? If this weren't the original pyramid builder, the series would have ended somewhere before we found him, wouldn't it? – ended and started over with the small ones. That's simple enough, isn't it?

'But he reproduces, or tries to. Before the third brick came out, there was a little rustle and out popped a whole stream of those little crystal balls. They're his spores, or eggs, or seeds – call 'em what you want. They went bouncing by across Xanthus just as they'd bounced by us back in the Mare Chronium. I've a hunch how they work, too – this is for your information, Leroy. I think the crystal shell of silica is no more than a protective covering, like an eggshell, and that the active principle is the smell inside. It's some sort of gas that attacks silicon, and if the shell is broken near a supply of that element, some reaction starts that ultimately develops into a beast like that one.'

'You should try!' exclaimed the little Frenchmen. 'We must break one to see!'

'Yeah? Well, I did. I smashed a couple against the sand. Would you like to come back in about ten thousand years to see if I planted some pyramid monsters? You'd most likely be able to tell by that time!' Jarvis paused and drew a deep breath. 'Lord! That queer creature! Do you picture it? Blind, deaf, nerveless, brainless – just a mechanism, and yet – immortal! Bound to go on making bricks, building pyramids, as long as silicon and oxygen exist, and even afterwards it'll just stop. It won't be dead. If the accidents of a million years bring it its food again, there it'll be, ready to run again, while brains and civilizations are part of the past. A queer beast – yet I met a stranger one!'

'If you did, it must have been in your dreams!' growled Harrison.

'You're right!' said Jarvis soberly. 'In a way, you're right. The dream-beast! That's the best name for it – and it's the most fiendish, terrifying creation one could imagine! More dangerous than a lion, more insidious than a snake!'

'Tell me!' begged Leroy. 'I must go see!'

'Not *this* devil!' He paused again. 'Well,' he resumed, 'Tweel and I left the pyramid creature and ploughed along through Xanthus. I was tired and a little disheartened by Putz's failure to pick me up, and Tweel's trilling got on my nerves, as did his flying nosedives. So I just strode along without a word, hour after hour across that monotonous desert.

'Towards mid-afternoon we came in sight of a low dark line on the horizon. I knew what it was. It was a canal; I'd crossed it in the rocket and it meant that we were just one-third of the way across Xanthus. Pleasant thought, wasn't it? And still, I was keeping up to schedule.

'We approached the canal slowly; I remembered that this one was bordered by a wide fringe of vegetation and that mud-heap city was on it.'

CHAPTER IV

The Dream-Beast

'I was tired, as I said. I kept thinking of a good hot meal, and then from that I jumped to reflections of how nice and home-like even Borneo would seem after this crazy planet, and from that, to thoughts of little old New York, and then to thinking about a girl I know there – Fancy Long. Know her?'

'Vision entertainer,' said Harrison. 'I've tuned her in. Nice blonde – dances and sings on the *Yerba Mate* hour.'

'That's her,' said Jarvis ungrammatically. 'I know her pretty well – just friends, get me? – though she came down to see us off in the *Ares*. Well, I was thinking about her, feeling pretty lonesome, and all the time we were approaching that line of rubbery plants.

'And then – I said, "What 'n hell!" and stared. And there she was – Fancy Long, standing plain as day under one of those crack-brained trees, and smiling and waving just the way I remembered her when we left!'

'Now you're nuts, too!' observed the Captain.

'Boy, I almost agreed with you! I stared and pinched myself and closed my eyes and then stared again – and every time, there was Fancy Long smiling and waving! Tweel saw something, too; he was trilling and clucking away, but I scarcely heard him. I was bounding towards her over the sand, too amazed even to ask myself questions.

'I wasn't twenty feet from her when Tweel caught me with one of his flying leaps. He grabbed my arm, yelling, "No – no – no!" in his squeaky voice. I tried to shake him off – he was as light as if he were built of bamboo – but he dug his claws in and yelled. And

27

finally some sort of sanity returned to me and I stopped less than ten feet from her. There she stood, looking as solid as Putz's head!'

'Vot?' said the engineer.

'She smiled and waved, and waved and smiled, and I stood there dumb as Leroy, while Tweel squeaked and chattered. I knew it couldn't be real, yet – there she was!

'Finally I said, "Fancy! Fancy Long!" She just kept on smiling and waving, but looking as real as if I hadn't left her thirty-seven million miles away.

'Tweel had his glass pistol out, pointing it at her. I grabbed him arm, but he tried to push me away. He pointed at her and said, "No breet! No breet!" and I understood that he meant that the Fancy Long thing wasn't alive. Man, my head was whirling!

'Still, it gave me the jitters to see him pointing his weapon at her. I don't know why I stood there watching him take careful aim, but I did. Then he squeezed the handle of his weapon; there was a little puff of steam, and Fancy Long was gone! And in her place was one of those writhing, black, rope-armed horrors like the one I'd saved Tweel from!

'The dream-beast! I stood there dizzy, watching it die while Tweel trilled and whistled. Finally he touched my arm, pointed at the twisting thing, and said, "You one-one-two, he one-one-two." After he'd repeated it eight or ten times, I got it. Do any of you?'

'Oui!' shrilled Leroy. 'Moi – je le comprends! He mean you think of something, the beast he know, and you see it! Un chien – a hungry dog, he would see the big bone with meat! Or smell it – not?'

'Right!' said Jarvis. 'The dream-beast uses its victim's longings and desires to trap its prey. The bird at nesting season would see its mate, the fox, prowling for its own prey, would see a helpless rabbit!'

'How he do?' queried Leroy.

'How do I know? How does a snake back on earth charm a bird into its very jaws? And aren't there deep-sea fish that lure their victims into their mouths? Lord!' Jarvis shuddered. 'Do you see how insidious the monster is? We're warned now – but henceforth we can't trust even our own eyes. You might see me – I might see one of you – and back of it may be nothing but another of those black horrors!'

'How'd your friend know?' asked the Captain abruptly.

'Tweel? I wonder! Perhaps he was thinking of something that couldn't possibly have interested me, and when I started to run, he realized that I saw something different and was warned. Or perhaps the dream-beast can only project a single vision, and Tweel saw what I saw – or nothing. I couldn't ask him. But it's just another proof that his intelligence is equal to ours or greater.'

'He's daffy, I tell you!' said Harrison. 'What makes you think his intellect ranks with the human?'

'Plenty of things! First, the pyramid-beast. He hadn't seen one before; he said as much. Yet he recognized it as a dead-alive automation of silicon.'

'He could have heard of it,' objected Harrison. 'He lives around here, you know.'

'Well, how about the language? I couldn't pick up a single idea of his and he learned six or seven words of mine. And do you realize what complex ideas he put over with no more than those six or seven words? The pyramid-monster – the dream-beast! In a single phrase he told me that one was a harmless automaton and the other a deadly hypnotist. What about that?'

'Huh!' said the Captain.

'*Huh* if you wish! Could you have done it knowing only six words of English? Could you go even further, as Tweel did, and tell me that another creature was of a sort of intelligence so different from ours that understanding was impossible – even more impossible than that between Tweel and me?'

'Eh? What was that?'

'Later. The point I'm making is that Tweel and his race are worthy of our friendship. Somewhere on Mars – and you'll find I'm right – is a civilization and culture equal to ours, and maybe more than equal. And communication is possible between them and us; Tweel proves that. It may take years of patient trial, for their minds are alien, but less alien than the next minds we encountered – if they *are* minds.'

'The next ones? What next ones?'

'The people of the mud-heap cities along the canals.' Jarvis frowned, then resumed his narrative. 'I thought the dream-beast and the silicon-monster were the strangest beings conceivable, but I was wrong. These creatures are still more alien, less understandable than either and far less comprehensible than Tweel, with whom friendship is possible, and even, by patience and concentration, the exchange of ideas.

'Well,' he continued, 'we left the dream-beast dying, dragging itself back into its hole, and we moved towards the canal. There was a carpet of that queer walking-grass scampering out of our way, and when we reached the bank, there was a yellow trickle of water flowing. The mound city I'd noticed from the rocket was a mile or so to the right and I was curious enough to want to take a look at it.

'It had seemed deserted from my previous glimpse of it, and if any creatures were lurking in it – well, Tweel and I were both armed. And by the way, that crystal weapon of Tweel's was an interesting device; I took a look at it after the dream-beast episode. It fired a little glass splinter, poisoned, I suppose, and I guess it held at least a hundred of 'em to a load. The propellant was steam – just plain steam!'

'Shteam!' echoed Putz. 'From vot comes shteam?'

'From water, of course! You could see the water through the transparent handle, and about a gill of another liquid, thick and yellowish. When Tweel squeezed the handle – there was no trigger – a drop of water and a drop of the yellow stuff squirted into the firing chamber, and the water vapourized – pop! – like that. It's not so difficult; I think we could develop the same principle. Concentrated sulphuric acid will heat water almost to boiling, and so will quicklime, and there's potassium and sodium –

'Of course, his weapon hadn't the range of mine, but it wasn't so bad in this thin air, and it *did* hold as many shots as a cowboy's gun in a Western movie. It was effective, too, at least against Martian life; I tried it out, aiming at one of the crazy plants, and darned if the plant didn't wither up and fall apart! That's why I think the glass splinters were poisoned.

'Anyway, we trudged along towards the mud-heap city and I began to wonder whether the city builders dug the canals. I pointed to the city and then at the canal, and Tweel said "No – no – no!" and gestured towards the south. I took it to mean that some other race had created the canal system, perhaps Tweel's people. I don't know; maybe there's still another intelligent race on the planet, or a dozen others. Mars is a queer little world.'

CHAPTER V

The Barrel-People

'A hundred yards from the city we crossed a sort of road – just a hard-packed mud trail, and then, all of a sudden, along came one of the mound builders!

'Man, talk about fantastic beings! It looked rather like a barrel trotting along on four legs with four other arms or tentacles. It had no head, just body and members and a row of eyes completely around it. The top end of the barrel-body was a diaphragm stretched as tight as a drum head, and that was all. It was pushing a little coppery cart and tore right past us like the proverbial bat out of Hell. It didn't even notice us, although I thought the eyes on my side shifted a little as it passed.

'A moment later another came along, pushing another empty cart. Same thing – it just scooted past us. Well, I wasn't going to be ignored by a bunch of barrels playing train, so when the third one approached, I planted myself in the way – ready to jump, of course, if the thing didn't stop.

'But it did. It stopped and set up a sort of drumming from the diaphragm on top. And I held out both hands and said mildly, "We are friends!" And what do you suppose the thing did?'

'Said, "Pleased to meet you," I'll bet!' suggested Harrison.

'I couldn't have been more surprised if it had! It drummed on its diaphragm, and then suddenly boomed out. "We are v-r-r-riends!" and gave its pushcart a vicious poke at me! I jumped aside, and away it went while I stared dumbly after it.

'A minute later another one came hurrying along. This one didn't pause, but simply drummed out, "We are v-r-r-riends!" and scurried by. How did it learn the phrase? Were all of the creatures in some sort of communication with each other? Were they all parts of

31

some central organism? I don't know, though I think Tweel does.

'Anyway, the creatures went sailing past us, every one greeting us with the same statement. It got to be funny; I never thought to find so many friends on this God-forsaken ball! Finally I made a puzzled gesture to Tweel; I guess he understood, for he said, "One-one-two – yes! – two-two-four – no!" Get it?'

'Sure,' said Harrison. 'It's a Martian nursery rhyme.'

'Yeah! Well, I was getting used to Tweel's symbolism, and I figured it out this way. "One-one-two – yes!" The creatures were intelligent. "Two-two-four – no!" Their intelligence was not of our order, but something different and beyond the logic of two and two is four. Maybe I missed his meaning. Perhaps he meant that their minds were of low degree, able to figure out the simple things – "One-one-two – yes!" – but not more difficult things – "Two-two-four – no!" But I think from what we saw later that he meant the other.

'After a few moments, the creatures came rushing back – first one, then another. Their pushcarts were full of stones, sand, chunks of rubbery plants, and such rubbish as that. They droned out their friendly greeting, which didn't really sound so friendly, and dashed on. The third one I assumed to be my first acquaintance and I decided to have another chat with him. I stepped into the path again and waited.

'Up he came, booming out his "We are v-r-r-riends" and stopped. I looked at him; four or five of his eyes looked at me. He tried his password again and gave a shove of his cart, but I stood firm. And then the – the dashed creature reached out one of his arms, and two finger-like nippers tweaked my nose!'

'Haw!' roared Harrison. 'Maybe the things have a sense of beauty!'

'Laugh!' grumbled Jarvis. 'I'd already had a nasty bump and a mean frostbite on that nose. Anyway, I yelled "Ouch!" and jumped aside and the creature dashed away; but from then on, their greeting was "We are v-r-r-riends! Ouch!" Queer beasts!

'Tweel and I followed the road squarely up to the nearest mound. The creatures were coming and going, paying us not the slightest attention, fetching their loads of rubbish. The road simply dived into an opening, and slanted down like an old mine, and in and out darted the barrel-people, greeting us with their eternal phrase.

'I looked in; there was a light somewhere below, and I was curious to see it. It didn't look like a flame or torch, you understand, but more like a civilized light, and I thought that I might get some clue as to the creatures' development. So in I went and Tweel tagged along, not without a few trills and twitters, however.

'The light was curious; it sputtered and flared like an old arc light, but came from a single black rod set in the wall of the corridor. It was electric, beyond doubt. The creatures were fairly civilized, apparently.

'Then I saw another light shining on something that glittered and I went on to look at that, but it was only a heap of shiny sand. I turned towards the entrance to leave, and the Devil take me if it wasn't gone!

'I suppose the corridor had curved, or I'd stepped into a side passage. Anyway, I walked back in the direction I thought we'd come, and all I saw was more dim-lit corridor. The place was a labyrinth! There was nothing but twisting passages running every way, lit by occasional lights, and now and then a creature running by, sometimes with a pushcart, sometimes without.

'Well, I wasn't much worried at first. Tweel and I had only come a few steps from the entrance. But every move we made after that seemed to get us in deeper. Finally I tried following one of the creatures with an empty cart, thinking that he'd be going out for his rubbish, but he ran around aimlessly, into one passage and out another. When he started dashing around a pillar like one of these Japanese waltzing mice, I gave up, dumped my water tank on the floor, and sat down.

'Tweel was as lost as I. I pointed up and he said "No – no – no!" in a sort of helpless trill. And we couldn't get any help from the natives; they paid us no attention at all, except to assure us they were friends – ouch!

'Lord! I don't know how many hours or days we wandered around there! I slept twice from sheer exhaustion; Tweel never seemed to need sleep. We tried following only the upward corridors, but they'd run uphill a ways and then curve downwards. The temperature in that damned ant-hill was constant; you couldn't tell night from day and after my first sleep I didn't know whether I'd slept one hour or thirteen, so I couldn't tell from my watch whether it was midnight or noon.

'We saw plenty of strange things. There were machines running in some of the corridors, but they didn't seem to be doing anything – just wheels turning. And several times I saw two barrel-beasts with a little one growing between them, joined to both.'

'Parthenogenesis!' exulted Leroy. 'Parthenogenesis by budding – like *les tulipes*!'

'If you say so, Frenchy,' agreed Jarvis. 'The things never noticed us at all, except, as I say, to greet us with "We are v-r-r-riends! Ouch!" They seemed to have no home-life of any sort, but just scurried around with their pushcarts, bringing in rubbish. And finally I discovered what they did with it.

'We'd had a little luck with a corridor, one that slanted upwards for a great distance. I was feeling that we ought to be close to the surface when suddenly the passage debouched into a domed chamber, the only one we'd seen. And man! – I felt like dancing when I saw what looked like daylight through a crevice in the roof.

'There was a – a sort of machine in the chamber, just an enormous wheel that turned slowly, and one of the creatures was in the act of dumping his rubbish below it. The wheel ground it with a crunch – sand, stones, plants, all into powder that sifted away somewhere. While we watched, others filed in, repeating the process, and that seemed to be all. No rhyme nor reason to the whole thing – but that's characteristic of this crazy planet. And there was another fact that's almost too bizarre to believe.

'One of the creatures, having dumped his load, pushed his cart aside with a crash and calmly shoved himself under the wheel! I watched him crushed, too stupefied to make a sound, and a moment later, another followed him! They were perfectly methodical about it, too; one of the cartless creatures took the abandoned pushcart.

'Tweel didn't seem surprised; I pointed out the next suicide to him, and he just gave the most human-like shrug imaginable, as much as to say, "What can I do about it?" He must have known more or less about these creatures.

'Then I saw something else. There was something beyond the wheel, something shining on a sort of low pedestal. I walked over; there was a little crystal about the size of an egg, fluorescing to beat Tophet. The light from it stung my hands and face, almost like a static discharge, and then I noticed another funny thing. Remember that wart I had on my left thumb? Look!' Jarvis extended his hand. 'It dried up and fell off – just like that! And my abused nose – say, the pain went out of it like magic! The thing had the property of hard X rays or gamma radiations, only more so; it destroyed diseased tissue and left healthy tissue unharmed!

'I was thinking what a present *that'd* be to take back to Mother Earth when a lot of racket interrupted. We dashed back to the other side of the wheel in time to see one of the pushcarts ground up. Some suicide had been careless, it seems.

'Then suddenly the creatures were booming and drumming all around us and their noise was decidedly menacing. A crowd of them advanced towards us; we backed out of what I thought was the passage we'd entered by, and they came rumbling after us, some pushing carts and some not. Crazy brutes! There was a whole chorus of "We are v-r-r-riends! Ouch!" I didn't like the "ouch"; it was rather suggestive.

'Tweel had his glass gun out and I dumped my water tank for greater freedom and got mine. We backed up the corridor with the barrel-beasts following – about twenty of them. Queer thing – the ones coming in with loaded carts moved past us inches away without a sign.

'Tweel must have noticed that. Suddenly, he snatched out that glowing coal cigar-lighter of his and touched a cartload of plant limbs. Puff! The whole load was burning – and the crazy beast pushing it went right along without a change of pace! It created some disturbance among our "V-r-r-riends", however – and then I noticed the smoke eddying and swirling past us, and sure enough, there was the entrance.

'I grabbed Tweel and out we dashed and after us our twenty pursuers. The daylight felt like Heaven, though I saw at first glance that the sun was all but set, and

35

that was bad, since I couldn't live outside my thermo-bag in a Martian night – at least, without a fire.

'And things got worse in a hurry. They cornered us in an angle between two mounds, and there we stood. I hadn't fired nor had Tweel; there wasn't any use in irritating the brutes. They stopped a little distance away and began their booming about friendship and ouches.

'Then things got still worse! A barrel-brute came out with a pushcart and they all grabbed into it and came out with handfuls of foot-long copper darts – sharp-looking ones – and all of a sudden one sailed past my ear – zing! And it was shoot or die then.

'We were doing pretty well for a while. We picked off the ones next to the pushcart and managed to keep the darts at a minimum, but suddenly there was a thunderous booming of "v-r-r-riends" and "ouches", and a whole army of 'em came out of their hole.

'Man! We were through and I knew it! Then I realized that Tweel wasn't. He could have leaped the mound behind us as easily as not. He was staying for me!

'Say, I could have cried if there'd been time! I'd liked Tweel from the first, but whether I'd have the gratitude to do what he was doing – suppose I *had* saved him from the first dream-beast – he'd done as much for me, hadn't he? I grabbed his arm, and said "Tweel", and pointed up, and he understood. He said, "No – no – no, Tick!" and popped away with his glass pistol.

'What could I do? I'd be a goner anyway when the sun set, but I couldn't explain that to him. I said, "Thanks, Tweel. You're a man!" and felt that I wasn't paying him any compliment at all. A man! There are mighty few men who'd do that.

'So I went "bang" with my gun and Tweel went "puff" with his, and the barrels were throwing darts and getting ready to rush us, and booming about being friends. I had given up hope. Then suddenly an angel dropped right down from Heaven in the shape of Putz, with his under-jets blasting the barrels into very small pieces!

'Wow! I let out a yell and dashed for the rocket; Putz opened the door and I went, laughing and crying and shouting! It was a moment or so before I remembered Tweel; I looked around in time to see him rising in one of his nosedives over the mound and away.

'I had a devil of a job arguing Putz into following! By the time we got the rocket aloft, darkness was down; you know how it comes here – like turning off a light. We sailed out over the desert and put down once or twice. I yelled "Tweel!" and yelled it a hundred times, I guess. We couldn't find him; he could travel like the wind and all I got – or else I imagined it – was a faint trilling twittering drifting out of the south. He'd gone, and damn it! I wish – I wish he hadn't!'

The four men of the *Ares* were silent – even the sardonic Harrison. At last little Leroy broke the stillness.

'I should like to see,' he murmured.

'Yeah,' said Harrison. 'And the wart cure. Too bad you missed that; it might be the cancer cure they've been hunting for a century and a half.'

'Oh, that!' muttered Jarvis gloomily. 'That's what started the fight!' He drew a glistening object from his pocket.

'Here it is.'

A MARTIAN ODYSSEY

The story was written in 1934. It was one of the first stories to deal with extraterrestrial beings realistically; that is, to suppose that they might really be alien.

Earlier stories set on Mars had used the name of the planet and a few salient facts, such as its possession of two moons, but no more. Except for that, the setting might just as well have been some fairy-tale extension of Earth. What's more, intelligent Martians were pictured as essentially Earthmen, differing only in superficial detail. In fact, Martian princesses were often human enough to be objects of romantic longing for Earthmen-heroes.

A Martian Odyssey changed all that. It was the first published science fiction story of Stanley G. Weinbaum who, at one bound, became the most popular author in the field. It was not just the realism of his alien other-world creatures, but it was also his light and easy style, a far cry from the creakiness of the writings of most of the s.f. authors of the early thirties. For two years, he retained his popularity and then, as suddenly as he came, he vanished, for in 1936, at the age of thirty-six, he died of cancer.

Weinbaum was careful, in this story, to keep his description of Mars realistic, but he could do so only in terms of the time in which it was written. At that time it was known that the Martian atmosphere was thinner than ours, but not exactly how much thinner. Nor was its composition known. Obviously, Weinbaum assumed it would be thick enough and have oxygen enough for a human being to be able to breathe without an extraneous air supply, although he was realistic enough to suppose men would have to be acclimated to the thin air. The Martian air, as pictured by Weinbaum, could also support quite complicated animal life and could support fires as well.

This, alas, has proved to be much too optimistic. Later information, including the data sent back by Mars-probes (thirty years after the story was written) make Weinbaum's picture of the planet impossible.

The expedition to Mars took place, according to Weinbaum, in the twenty-first century. This may turn out to be correct, but he had it take place ten years after the first landing on the Moon and less than twenty years after the invention of the 'atomic blast'.

The atomic bomb was first exploded in 1945 (probably at least half a century sooner than Weinbaum expected) which would have made the first Mars landing come before 1965. Then, too, Weinbaum says, 'Remember how the public mobbed the first Moon pictures?' Clearly, he is thinking of moving pictures, and never envisaged the live television coverage of the Moon landings.

A particularly fascinating part of Weinbaum's picture of Martian life is that of the 'pyramid being'. Silicon is similar to carbon in many of its chemical properties and in its electronic structure, so that one might imagine complicated molecules built out of long chains and rings of silicon atoms instead of carbon atoms. Unfortunately, silicon atoms are sufficiently larger than carbon atoms to make the chemical bonds between the former much weaker than between the latter. Even short chains of silicon atoms are quite unstable.

Furthermore, Weinbaum makes the implication that the pyramid being lived on elementary silicon, oxidizing it for energy and producing silicon dioxide (also

38

called silica, or quartz). This, too, is most unlikely, for silicon never appears in elementary form in the Earth's crust and is almost certain not to do so in the Martian crust, either.

Despite the scientific shortcomings in the story, it has held up over the decades. In 1969, the membership of the Science Fiction Writers of America selected the best science fiction short stories of all time and *A Martian Odyssey* finished in second place.

Questions and Suggestions

1. The attempts of Dick Jarvis to communicate with Tweel remind one of modern suggestions at communication with possible intelligences from other planetary systems. How would you use radio signals to communicate with an alien intelligence which does not know your language or anything about you? How would you describe your own appearance?

2. Look up the current information about the Martian surface and atmosphere and decide how the story would have to be changed to meet it. What characteristics of the surface does Weinbaum mention that aren't there; what does he leave out that *are* there?

3. Is Weinbaum correct in suggesting that Mercury is not visible to the naked eye from Mars? How bright would Mercury seem and how far from the Sun would it appear to be at most? How would Earth appear as seen from Mars? How about our Moon?

4. Look up the chemistry of silicon and determine whether it might conceivably form the basis of life in some form a little more complicated than pure chains of silicon atoms? Are there any other non-carbon chemistries that might form a basis for life by building up sufficiently complicated molecules?

2. NIGHT

Don A. Stuart

Condon was staring through the glasses with a face tense and drawn, all his attention utterly concentrated on that one almost invisible speck infinitely far up in the blue sky, and saying over and over again in the most horribly absent-minded way, 'My Lord – my Lord—'

Suddenly he shivered and looked down at me, sheer agony in his face. 'He's never coming down. Don, he's never coming down—'

I knew it, too – knew it as solidly as I knew the knowledge was impossible. But I smiled and said: 'Oh, I wouldn't say that. If anything, I'd fear his coming down. What goes up comes down.'

Major Condon trembled all over. His mouth worked horribly for a moment before he could speak. 'Talbot – I'm scared – I'm horribly scared. You know – you're his assistant – you know he's trying to defy gravity. Men aren't meant to – it's wrong – wrong—'

His eyes were glued on those binoculars again, with the same terrible tensity, and now he was saying over and over in that absent-minded way, 'wrong – wrong – wrong—'

Simultaneously he stiffened, and stopped. The dozen or so other men standing on that lonely little emergency field stiffened; then the major crumpled to the ground. I've never before seen a man faint, let alone an army officer with a D.S. medal. I didn't stop to help him, because I knew something had happened. I grabbed the glasses.

Far, far up in the sky was that little orange speck – far, where there is almost no air, and he had been forced to wear a stratosphere suit with a little alcohol heater. The broad, orange wings were overlaid now with a faint-glowing, pearl-grey light. And it was falling. Slowly, at first, circling aimlessly downward. Then it dipped, rose, and somehow went into a tail spin.

It was horrible. I know I must have breathed, but it didn't seem so. It took minutes for it to fall those miles, despite the speed. Eventually it whipped out of that tail spin – through sheer speed, whipped out and into a power dive. It was a ghastly, flying coffin, hurtling at more than half a thousand miles an hour when it reached the Earth, some fifteen miles away.

The ground trembled, and the air shook with the crash of it. We were in the cars and roaring across the ground long before it hit. I was in Bob's car, with Jeff, his laboratory technician – Bob's little roadster he'd never need again. The engine picked up quickly, and we were going seventy before we left the field, jumped a shallow ditch and hit the road – the deserted concrete road that led on towards where he must be. The engine roared as Jeff clamped down on the accelerator. Dimly, I heard the major's big car coming along behind us.

Jeff drove like a maniac, but I didn't notice. I knew the thing had done ninety-five but I think we must have done more. The wind whipped tears in my eyes so I couldn't be sure whether I saw mounting smoke and flame or not. With Diesel fuel there shouldn't be – but that plane had been doing things it shouldn't. It had been trying out Carter's anti-gravity coil.

We shot up the flat, straight road across wide, level country, the wind moaning a requiem about the car. Far ahead I saw the side road that must lead off towards where Bob should be, and lurched to the braking of the car, the whine and sing of violently shrieking tyres, then to the skidding corner. It was a sand road; we slithered down it and for all the lightness and power, we slowed to sixty-five, clinging to the seat as the soft sand gripped and clung.

Violently Jeff twisted into a branching cow path, and somehow the springs took it. We braked to a stop a quarter of a mile from the plane.

It was in a fenced field of pasture and wood lot. We leaped the fence, and raced towards it; Jeff got there first, just as the major's car shrieked to a stop behind ours.

The major was cold and pale when he reached us. 'Dead,' he stated.

And I was very much colder and probably several times as pale. 'I don't know!' I moaned. 'He isn't there!'

'Not there!' The major almost screamed it. 'He must

be – he has to be. He had no parachute – wouldn't take one. They say he didn't jump—'

I pointed to the plane, and wiped a little cold sweat from my forehead. I felt clammy all over, and my spine prickled. The solid steel of the huge Diesel engine was driven through the stump of a tree, down into the ground perhaps eight or nine feet, and the dirt and rock had splashed under that blow like wet mud.

The wings were on the other side of the field, flattened, twisted straws of dural alloy. The fuselage of the ship was a perfect silhouette – a longitudinal projection that had flattened in on itself, each separate section stopping only as it hit the ground.

The great torus coil with its strangely twined wrappings of hair-fine bismuth wire was intact! And bent over it, twisted, utterly wrecked by the impact, was the main-wing stringer – the great dural-alloy beam that supported most of the ship's weight in the air. It was battered, crushed on those hair-fine fragile bismuth wires – and not one of them was twisted or displaced or so much as skinned. The back frame of the ponderous Diesel engine – the heavy supercharger was the anvil of that combination – was cracked and splintered. And not one wire of the hellish bismuth coil was strained or skinned or displaced.

And the red pulp that should have been there – the red pulp that had been a man – wasn't. It simply wasn't there at all. He hadn't left the plane. In the clear, cloudless air, we could see that. He was gone.

We examined it, of course. A farmer came, and another, and looked, and talked. Then several farmers came in old, dilapidated cars with their wives and families, and watched.

We set the owner of the property on watch and went away – went back to the city for workmen and a truck with a derrick. Dusk was falling. It would be morning before we could do anything, so we went away.

Five of us – the major of the army air force, Jeff Rodney, the two Douglass Co. men whose names I never remembered and I – sat in my – our – room. Bob's and Jeff's and mine. We'd been sitting there for hours trying to talk, trying to think, trying to remember every little detail, and trying to forget every ghastly detail. We couldn't remember the detail that explained it, nor forget the details that rode and harried us.

And the telephone rang. I started. Then slowly got up and answered. A strange voice, flat and rather unpleasant, said: 'Mr. Talbot?'

'Yes.'

It was Sam Gantry, the farmer we'd left on watch. 'There's a man here.'

'Yes? What does he want?'

'I dunno. I dunno where he came from. He's either dead or out cold. Gotta funny kind of an aviator suit on, with a glass face on it. He looks all blue, so I guess he's dead.'

'Lord! Bob! Did you take that helmet off?' I roared.

'No, sir, no – no, sir. We just left him the way he was.'

'His tanks have run out. Listen. Take a hammer, a wrench, anything, and break that glass faceplate! Quick! We'll be there.'

Jeff was moving. The major was, too, and the others. I made a grab for the half-empty bottle of Scotch, started out, and ducked back into the closet. With the oxygen bottle under my arm I jumped into the crowded little roadster just as Jeff started it moving. He turned on the horn, and left it that way.

We dodged, twisted, jumped and stopped with jerks in traffic, then leaped into smooth, roaring speed out towards the farmer's field. The turns were familiar now; we scarcely slowed for them, slewing around them. This time Jeff charged through the wire fence. A headlight popped; there was a shrill scream of wire, the wicked *zing* of wire scratching across the hood and mud guards, and we were bouncing across the field.

There were two lanterns on the ground; three men carried others; more men squatted down beside a still figure garbed in a fantastic, bulging, airproof stratosphere suit. They looked at us, open-mouthed as we skidded to a halt, moving aside as the major leaped out and dashed over with the Scotch. I followed close behind with the oxygen bottle.

Bob's faceplate was shattered, his face blue, his lips blue and flecked with froth. A long gash across his cheek from the shattered glass bled slowly. The major lifted his head without a word, and glass tinkled inside the helmet as he tried to force a little whisky down his throat.

43

'Wait!' I called. 'Major, give him artificial respiration, and this will bring him round quicker – better.' The major nodded, and rose, rubbing his arm with a peculiar expression.

'That's cold!' he said, as he flipped Bob over, and straddled his back. I held the oxygen bottle under Bob's nose as the major swung back in an arc, and let the raw, cold oxygen gas flow into his nostrils.

In ten seconds Bob coughed, gurgled, coughed violently, and took a deep shuddering breath. His face turned pink almost instantly under that lungful of oxygen, and I noticed with some surprise that he seemed to exhale almost nothing, his body absorbing the oxygen rapidly.

He coughed again; then: 'I could breathe a heck of a sight better if you'd get off my back,' he said. The major jumped up, and Bob turned over and sat up. He waved me aside, and spat. 'I'm – all right,' he said softly.

'Lord, man, what happened?' demanded the major.

Bob sat silent for a minute. His eyes had the strangest look – a hungry look – as he gazed about him. He looked at the trees beyond and at the silent, watching men in the light of the lanterns; then up, up to where a myriad stars gleamed and danced and flickered in the clear night sky.

'I'm back,' he said softly. Then suddenly he shivered, and looked horribly afraid. 'But – I'll have to be – then – too.'

He looked at the major for a minute, and smiled faintly. And at the two Douglass Co. men. 'Your plane was all right. I started up on the wings, as arranged, went way up, till I thought surely I was at a safe height, where the air wasn't too dense and the field surely wouldn't reach to Earth – Lord! – reach to Earth! I didn't guess how far that field extended. It touched Earth – twice.

'I was at forty-five thousand when I decided it was safe, and cut the engine. It died, and the stillness shocked me. It was so quiet. So quiet.

'I turned on the coil circuit, and the dynamotor began to hum as the tubes warmed up. And then – the field hit me. It paralysed me in an instant. I never had a chance to break the circuit, though I knew instantly something was wrong – terribly wrong. But the very

44

first thing it did was to paralyse me, and I had to sit there and watch the instruments climb to positions and meanings they were never meant for.

'I realised I alone was being affected by that coil — I alone, sitting directly over it. I stared at the meters and they began to fade, began to seem transparent, unreal. And as they faded into blankness I saw clear sky beyond them; then for a hundredth of a second, like some effect of persistence of vision, I thought I saw the plane falling, twisting down at incredible speed, and the light faded as the Sun seemed to rocket suddenly across the sky and vanish.

'I don't know how long I was in that paralysed condition, where there was only blankness — neither dark nor light nor time nor any form — but I breathed many times. Finally, form crawled and writhed into the blankness, and seemed to solidify beneath me as, abruptly, the blankness gave way to a dull red light. I was falling.

'I thought instantly of the forty-five thousand feet that lay between me and the solid Earth, and stiffened automatically in terror. And in the same instant I landed in a deep blanket of white snow, stained by the red light that lighted the world.

'Cold. Cold — it tore into me like the fang of a savage animal. What cold! The cold of ultimate death. It ripped through that thick, insulated suit and slashed at me viciously, as though there were no insulation there. I shivered so violently I could scarcely turn up the alcohol valves. You know I carried alcohol tanks and catalyst grids for heating, because the only electric fields I wanted were those of the apparatus. Even used a Diesel instead of gas engine.

'I thank the Lord for that then. I realised that whatever had happened I was in a spot indescribably cold and desolate. And in the same instant, realised that the sky was black. Blacker than the blackest night, and yet before me the snow field stretched to infinity, tainted by the blood-red light, and my shadow crawled in darker red at my feet.

'I turned around. As far as the eye could see in three directions the land swept off in very low, very slightly rolling hills, almost plains — red plains of snow dyed with the dripping light of sunset. I thought.

'In the fourth direction, a wall — a wall that put the

45

Great Wall of China to shame – loomed up half a mile – a blood-red wall that had the lustre of metal. It stretched across the horizon, and looked a scant hundred yards away, for the air was utterly clear. I turned up my alcohol burners a bit more and felt a little better.

'Something jerked my head around like a giant hand – a sudden thought. I stared at the Sun and gulped. It was four times – six times – the size of the Sun I knew. And it wasn't setting. It was forty-five degrees from the horizon. It was red. Blood-red. And there wasn't the slightest bit of radiant heat reaching my face from it. That Sun was cold.

'I'd just automatically assumed I was still on Earth, whatever else might have happened, but now I knew I couldn't be. It must be another planet of another sun – a frozen planet – for that snow was frozen air. I knew it absolutely. A frozen planet of a dead sun.

'And then I changed even that. I looked up at the black sky above me, and in all the vast black bowl of the heavens, not three-score stars were visible. Dim, red stars, with one single sun that stood out for its brillance – a yellowish-red sun perhaps a tenth as bright as our Sun, but a monster here. It was another – a dead – space. For if that snow was frozen air, the only atmosphere must have been neon and helium. There wasn't any hazy air to stop the light of the stars, and that dim, red sun didn't obscure them with its light. The stars were gone.

'In that glimpse, my mind began working by itself; I was scared.

'Scared? I was so scared I was afraid I was going to be sick. Because right then I knew I was never coming back. When I felt that cold, I'd wondered when my oxygen bottles would give out, if I'd get back before they did. Now it was not a worry. It was simply the limiting factor on an already-determined thing, the setting on the time bomb. I had just so much more time before I died right there.

'My mind was working out things, working them out all by itself, and giving answers I didn't want, didn't want to know about. For some reason it persisted in considering this was Earth, and the conviction became more and more fixed. It was right. That was Earth. And it was old Sol. Old – old Sol. It was the time axis that

46

coil distorted – not gravity at all. My mind worked that our with a logic as cold as that planet.

'If it was time it had distorted, and this was Earth, then it had distorted time beyond imagining to an extent as meaningless to our minds as the distance a hundred million light years is. It was simply vast – incalculable. The Sun was dead. The Earth was dead. And Earth was already, in our time, two billions of years old, and in all that geological time, the Sun had not changed measurably. Then how long was it since my time? The Sun was dead. The very stars were dead. It must have been, I thought even then, billions on billions of years. And I grossly underestimated it.

'The world was old – old – old. The very rocks and ground radiated a crushing aura of incredible age. It was older, older than – but what is there? Older than the hills? Hills? Gosh, they'd been born and died and been born and worn away again, a million, a score of million times! Old as the stars? No, that wouldn't do. The stars were dead – then.

'I looked again at the metal wall, and set out for it, and the aura of age washed up at me, and dragged at me, and tried to stop this motion when all motion should have ceased. And the thin, unutterably cold wind whined in dead protest at me, and pulled at me with the ghost hands of the million millon million that had been born and lived and died in the countless ages before I was born.

'I wondered as I went. I didn't think clearly; for the dead aura of the dead planet pulled at me. Age. The stars were dying, dead. They were huddled there in space, like decrepit old men, huddling for warmth. The galaxy was shrunk. So tiny, it wasn't a thousand light years across, the stars were separated by miles where there had been light years. The magnificent, proudly sprawling universe I had known, that flung itself across a million million light years, that flung radiant energy through space by the millions of millions of tons was – gone.

'It was dying – a dying miser that hoarded its last broken dregs of energy in a tiny cramped space. It was broken and shattered. A thousand billion years before the cosmical constant had been dropped from that broken universe. The cosmical constant that flung giant galaxies whirling apart with ever greater speed had no

47

place here. It had hurled the universe in broken fragments, till each spattered bit felt the chill of loneliness, and wrapped space about itself, to become a universe in itself while the flaming galaxies vanished.

'That had happened so long ago that the writing it had left in the fabric of space itself had worn away. Only the gravity constant remained, the hoarding constant, that drew things together, and slowly the galaxy collapsed, shrunken and old, a withered mummy.

'The very atoms were dead. The light was cold; even the red light made things look older, colder. There was no youth in the universe. I didn't belong, and the faint protesting rustle of the infinitely cold wind about me moved the snow in muted, futile protest, resenting my intrusion from a time when things were young. It whinnied at me feebly, and chilled the youth of me.

'I plodded on and on, and always the metal wall retreated, like one of those desert mirages. I was too stupefied by the age of the thing to wonder; I just walked on.

I was getting nearer, though. The wall was real; it was fixed. As I drew slowly nearer, the polished sheen of the wall died and the last dregs of hope died. I'd thought there might be someone still living behind that wall. Besides who could build such a thing might be able to live even here. But I couldn't stop then; I just went on. The wall was broken and cracked. It wasn't a wall I'd seen; it was a series of broken walls, knitted by distance to a smooth front.

'There was no weather to age them, only the faintest stirring of faint, dead winds – winds of neon and helium, inert and uncorroding – as dead and inert as the universe. The city had been dead a score of billions of years. That city was dead for a time ten times longer than the age of our planet today. But nothing destroyed it. Earth was dead – too dead to suffer the racking pains of life. The air was dead, too dead to scrape away metal.

'But the universe itself was dead. There was no cosmic radiation then to finally level the walls by atomic disintegration. There had been a wall – a single metal wall. Something – perhaps a last wandering meteor – had chanced on it in a time incalculably remote, and broken it. I entered through the great gap. Snow covered the city – soft, white snow. The great red sun stood still just where it was. Earth's restless rotation had long since been stilled – long, long since.

'There were dead gardens above, and I wandered up to them. That was really what convinced me it was a human city, on Earth. There were frozen huddled heaps that once might have been men. Little fellows with fear forever frozen on their faces huddled helplessly over something that once must have been a heating device. Dead perhaps, since the last storm old Earth had known, tens of billions of years before.

'I went down. There were vastnesses in that city. It was huge. It stretched forever, it seemed, on and on, in its deadness. Machines, machines everywhere. And the machines were dead, too. I went down, down where I thought a bit of light and heat might linger. I didn't know then how long death had been there; those corpses looked so fresh, preserved by the eternal cold.

'It grew dark down below, and only through rents and breaks did that bloody light seep in. Down and down, till I was below the level of the dead surface. The white snow persisted, and then I came to the cause of that final, sudden death. I could understand then. More and more I had puzzled, for those machines I'd seen I knew were far and beyond anything we ever conceived – machines of perfection, self-repairing, and self-energizing, self-perpetuating. They could make duplicates of themselves, and duplicate other, needed machines; they were intended to be eternal, everlasting.

'But the designers couldn't cope with some things that were beyond even their majestic imaginations – the imaginations that conceived these cities that had lived beyond –, a million times beyond – what they had dreamed. They must have conceived some vague future. But not a future when the Earth died, and the Sun died, and even the universe itself died.

'Cold had killed them. They had heating arrangements, devices intended to maintain forever the normal temperature despite the wildest variations of the weather. But in every electrical machine, resistances, balance resistances, and induction coils, balance condensers, and other inductances. And cold, stark, spatial cold, through ages, threw them off. Despite the heaters, cold crept in colder – cold that made their resistance balances and their induction coils superconductors! That destroyed the city. Superconduction – like the elimination of friction, on which all things must rest. It is a drag and a thing engineers fight forever. Resistance and friction must finally be the rest and the base of all things, the force that holds the great red bolts firm and the brakes that stop the machines when needed.

'Electrical resistance died in the cold and the wonderful machines stopped for the replacement of defective parts. And when they were replaced, they, too, were defective. For what months must that constant stop – replacement – start – stop – replacement have gone on before, at last defeated forever, those vast machines must bow in surrender to the inevitable? Cold had defeated them by defeating and removing the greatest obstacle of the engineers that built them – resistance.

'They must have struggled forever – as we would say – through a hundred billion years against encroaching harshness of nature, forever replacing worn, defective parts. At last, defeated forever, the great power plants, fed by dying atoms, had been forced into eternal idleness and cold. Cold conquered them at last.

'They didn't blow up. Nowhere did I see a wrecked machine; always they had stopped automatically when the defective resistance made it impossible to continue. The stored energy that was meant to re-start those machines after repairs had been made had long since leaked out. Never again could they move, I knew.

'I wondered how long they had been, how long they had gone on and on, long after the human need of them had vanished. For that vast city contained only a very few humans at the end. What untold ages of lonely functioning perfection had stretched behind those at-last-defeated mechanisms?

'I wandered out, to see perhaps more, before the necessary end came to me, too. Through the city of death. Everywhere little self-contained machines, cleaning machines that had kept that perfect city orderly and neat stood helpless and crushed by eternity and cold. They must have continued functioning for years after the great central power stations failed, for each contained its own store of energy, needing only occasional recharge from the central stations.

'I could see where breaks had occurred in the city, and, clustered about those breaks were motionless repair machines, their mechanisms in positions of work, the débris cleared away and carefully stacked on motionless trucks. The new beams and plates were partly attached, partly fixed and left, as the last dregs of their energy was fruitlessly expended in the last, dying attempts of that great body to repair itself. The death wounds lay unmended.

'I started back up. Up to the top of the city. It was a long climb, an infinite, weary climb, up half a mile of winding ramps, past deserted, dead homes; past, here and there, shops and restaurants; past motionless little automative passenger cars.

'Up and up, to the crowning gardens that lay stiff and brittle and frozen. The breaking of the roof must have caused a sudden chill, for their leaves lay green in sheaths of white, frozen air. Brittle grass, green and perfect to the touch. Flowers, blooming in wonderful perfection showed still; they didn't seem dead, but it didn't seem they could be otherwise under the blanket of cold.

'Did you ever sit up with a corpse?' Bob looked up at us – through us. 'I had to once, in my little home town where they always did that. I sat with a few neighbours while the man died before my eyes. I knew he must die when I came there. He died – and I sat there all night while the neighbours filed out, one by one, and the quiet settled. The quiet of the dead.

'I had to again. I was sitting with a corpse then. The corpse of a dead world in a dead universe, and the quiet didn't have to settle there; it had settled a billion years ago, and only my coming had stirred those feeble, protesting ghosts of eon-dead hopes of that planet to softly whining protest – protest the wind tried to sob to me, the dead wind of the dead gases. I'll never be able to call them inert gases again. I know. I know they are dead gases, the dead gases of dead worlds.

'And above, through the cracked crystal of the roof, the dying suns looked down on the dead city. I couldn't stay there, I went down. Down under layer after layer of buildings, buildings of gleaming metal that reflected the dim, blood light of the Sun outside in carmine stains. I went down and down, down to the machines again. But even there hopelessness seemed more intense. Again I saw that agonizing struggle of the eternally faithful machines trying to repair themselves once more to serve the masters who were dead a million million years. I could see it again in the frozen, exhausted postures of

51

the repair machines, stilled forever in their hopeless endeavours, the last poor dregs of energy spilled in fruitless conflict with time.

'It mattered little. Time himself was dying now, dying with the city and the planet and the universe he had killed.

'But those machines had tried so hard to serve again – and failed. Now they could never try again. Even they – the deathless machines – were dead.

'I went out again, away from those machines, out into the illimitable corridors, on the edge of the city. I could not penetrate far before the darkness became as absolute as the cold. I passed the shops where goods, untouched by time in this cold, still beckoned those strange humans, but humans for all that; beckoned the masters of the machines that were no more. I vaguely entered one to see what manner of things they used in that time.

'I nearly screamed at the motion of the thing in there, heard dimly through my suit the strangely softened sounds it made in the thin air. I watched it stagger twice – and topple. I cannot guess what manner of storage cells they had – save that they were marvellous beyond imagination. That stored energy that somehow I had released by entering was some last dreg that had remained through a time as old as our planet now. Its voice was stilled forever. But it drove me out – on.

'It had died while I watched. But somehow it made me more curious. I wondered again, less oppressed by utter death. Still, some untapped energy remained in this place, stored unimaginably. I looked more keenly, watched more closely. And when I saw a screen in one office, I wondered. It was a screen. I could see readily it was television of some type. Exploratively, I touched a stud. Sound! A humming, soft sound!

'To my mind leaped a picture of a system of these. There must be – interconnected – a vast central office somewhere with vaster accumulator cells, or huge, so tremendous in their power once, that even the little microfraction that remained was great. A storage system untouchable to the repair machines – the helpless, hopeless power machines.

'In an instant I was alive again with hope. There was a strange series of studs and dials, unknown devices. I pulled back on the stud I had pressed, and stood trembling, wondering. Was there hope?

'Then the thought died. What hope? The city was dead. Not merely that. It had been dead, dead for untold time. Then the whole planet was dead. With whom might I connect? There were none on the whole planet, so what mattered it that there was a communication system.

'I looked at the thing more blankly. Had there been — how could I interpret its multitudinous devices? There was a thing on one side that made me think of a telephone dial for some reason. A pointer over a metal sheet engraved with nine symbols in a circle under the arrow of the pointer. Now the pointer was over what was either the first or the last of these.

'Clumsily, in these gloves, I fingered one of the little symbol buttons inlaid in the metal. There was an unexpected click, a light glowed on the screen, a lighted image! It was a simple projection — but what a projection! A three-dimensional sphere floated, turning slowly before my eyes, turning majestically. And I nearly fell as understanding flooded me abruptly. The pointer was a selector! The studs beneath the pointer I understood! Nine of them. One after the other I pressed, and nine spheres — each different — swam before me.

'And right there I stopped and did some hard thinking. Nine spheres. Nine planets. Earth was shown first — a strange planet to me, but one I knew from the relative size and the position of the pointer must be Earth — then, in order, the other eight.

'Now — might there be life? Yes. In those nine worlds there might be, somewhere.

'Where? Mercury — nearest the Sun? No, the Sun was too dead, too cold, even for warmth there. And Mercury was too small. I knew, even as I thought, that I'd have one good chance because whatever means they had for communication wouldn't work without tremendous power. If those incredible storage cells had the power for even one shot, they had no more. Somehow I guessed that this apparatus might incorporate no resistance whatever. Here would be only very high frequency alternating current, and only condensers and inductances would be used in it. Supercooling didn't bother them any. It improved them. Not like the immense direct-current power machinery.

'But where to try? Jupiter? That was big. And then I saw what the solution must be. Cold had ruined these machines, thrown them off by making them too-perfect conductors. Because they weren't designed to defend themselves against spatial cold. But the machines – if there were any – on Pluto for instance, must originally have been designed for just such conditions; There it had always been cold. There it always would be cold.

'I looked at that thing with an intensity that should have driven my bare eyesight to Pluto. It was a hope. My only hope. But – how to signal Pluto They could not understand! If there were any 'they'.

'So I had to guess – and hope. Somehow, I knew, there must be some means of calling the intelligent attendant, that the user might get aid. There was a bank of little studs – twelve of them – with twelve symbols, each different, in the centre of the panel, grouped in four rows of three. I guessed. Duo-decimal system.

'Talk of the problems of interplanetary communication! Was there ever such a one? The problem of an anachronism in the city of the dead on a dead planet, seeking life somewhere, somehow.

'There were two studs, off by themselves, separate from the twelve – one green, one red. Again I guessed. Each of these had a complex series of symbols on it, so I turned the pointer on the right to Pluto, wavered, and turned it to Neptune. Pluto was farther. Neptune had been cold enough; the machines would still be working there, and it would be, perhaps, less of a strain on the dregs of energy that might remain.

'I depressed the green symbol hoping I had guessed truly, that red still meant danger, trouble and wrongness to men when that was built – that it meant release and cancellation for a wrongly pressed key. That left green to be an operative call signal.

'Nothing happened. The green key alone was not enough. I looked again, pressed the green key and that stud I had first pressed.

'The thing hummed again. But it was deeper note now, an entirely different sound, and there was a frenzied clicking inside. Then the green stud ticked back at me. The Neptune key under the pointer glowed softly; the screen began to shimmer with a greyish light. And, abruptly, the humming groaned as though at a terrific overload; the screen turned dull; the little signal light under Neptune's key grew dim. The signal was being sent – hurled out.

'Minute after minute I stood there, staring. The screen grew very slowly, very gently duller, duller. The energy was fading. The last stored driblet was being hurled away – away into space. "Oh," I groaned, "it's hopeless – hopeless to—"

'I'd realized the thing would take hours to get to that distant planet, travelling at the speed of light, even if it had been correctly aligned. But the machinery that should have done that through the years probably had long since failed for lack of power.

'But I stood there till the groaning motors ceased altogether and the screen was as dark as I'd found it, the signal light black. I released the stud then, and backed away, dazed by the utter collapse of an insane hope. Experimentally I pressed the Neptune symbol again. So little power was left now, that only the faintest wash of murky light projected the Neptune image, little energy as that would have consumed.

'I went out. Bitter. Hopeless. Earth's last picture was long, long since painted – and mine had been the hand that spent Earth's last poor resource. To its utter exhaustion, the eternal city had strived to serve the race that created it, and I, from the dawn of time had, at the end of time, drained its last poor atom of life. The thing was a thing done.

"Slowly I went back to the roof and the dying suns. Up the miles of winding ramp that climbed a half mile straight up. I went slowly – only life knows haste – and I was of the dead.

'I found a bench up there – a carved bench of metal in the midst of a riot of colourful, frozen flowers. I sat down, and looked out across the frozen city to the frozen world beyond, and the freezing red Sun.

'I do not know how long I sat there. And then something whispered in my mind.

"We sought you at the television machine."

'I leaped from the bench and stared wildly about me.

'It was floating in the air – a shining dirigible of metal, ruby-red in that light, twenty feet long, perhaps ten in diameter, bright, warm orange light gleaming from its ports. I stared at it in amazement.

'"It – it worked!" I gasped.

'"The beam carried barely enough energy to energize

the amplifiers when it reached Neptune, however," replied the creature in the machine.

'I couldn't see him – I knew I wasn't hearing him, but somehow that didn't surprise me.

' "Your oxygen has almost entirely given out, and I believe your mind is suffering from lack of oxygen. I would suggest you enter the lock; there is air in here."

'I don't know how he knew, but the gauges confirmed his statement. The oxygen was pretty nearly gone. I had perhaps another hours' supply if I opened the valves wide – but it was a most uncomfortably near thing, even so.

'I got in. I was beaming, joyous. There was life. This universe was not so dead as I had supposed. Not on Earth, perhaps, but only because they did not choose! They had space ships! Eagerly I climbed in, a strange thrill running through my body as I crossed the threshold of the lock. The door closed behind me with a soft *shush* on its soft gaskets, locked, and a pump whined somewhere for a moment; then the inner door opened. I stepped in – and instantly turned off my alcohol burners. There was heat – heat and light and air!

'In a moment I had the outer lacings loose, and the inner zipper down. Thirty seconds later I stepped out of the suit, and took a deep breath. The air was clean and sweet and warm, invigorating, fresh-smelling, as though it had blown over miles of green, Sun-warmed fields. It smelled alive, and young.

'Then I looked for the men who had come for me There was none. In the nose of the ship, by the controls, floated a four-foot globe of metal, softly glowing with a warm, golden light. The light pulsed slowly or swiftly with the rhythm of his thoughts, and I knew that this was the one who had spoken to me.

' "You had expected a human?" he thought to me. "There are no more. There have been none for a time I cannot express in your mind. Ah, yes, you have a mathematical means of expression, but no understanding of that time, so it is useless. But the last of humanity was allowed to end before the Sun changed from the original G-O stage – a very, very long time ago."

'I looked at him and wondered. Where was he from? Who – what – what manner of thing? Was it an armour-encased living creature or another of the perfect machines?

56

'I felt him watching my mind operate, pulsing softly in his golden light. And suddenly I thought to look out of the ports. The dim red suns were wheeling across those ports at an unbelievable rate. Earth was long since gone. As I looked, a dim, incredibly dim, red disc suddenly appeared, expanded – and I looked in awe at Neptune.

'The planet was scarcely visible when we were already within a dozen millions of miles. It was a jewelled world. Cities – the great, perfect cities – still glowed. They glowed in soft, golden light above, and below, the harsher, brighter blue of mercury vapour lighted them.

'He was speaking again. "We are machines – the ultimate development of man's machines. Man was almost gone when we came.

' "With what we have learned in the uncounted dusty mega-years since, we might have been able to save him. We could not then. It was better, wiser, that man end than that he sink down so low as he must, eventually. Evolution is the rise under pressure. Devolution is the gradual sinking that comes when there is no pressure – and there is no end to it. Life vanished from this system – a dusty infinity I cannot sort in my memory – my type memory, truly, for I have complete all the memories of those that went before me that I replace. But my memory cannot stretch back to that time you think of – a time when the constellations—

' "It is useless to try. Those memories are buried under others, and those still buried under the weight of a billion centuries.

' "We enter" – he named a city; I cannot reproduce that name – "now. You must return to Earth though in some seven and a quarter of your days, for the magnetic axis stretches back in collapsing field strains. I will be able to inject you into it, I believe."

'So I entered that city, the living city of machines, that had been when time and the universe were young.

'I did not know then that, when all this universe had dissolved away, when the last sun was black and cold, scattered dust in a fragment of a scattered universe, this planet with its machine cities would go on – a last speck of warm light in a long-dead universe. I did not know then.

' "You still wonder that we let man die out?" asked

57

the machine. "It was best. In another brief million years he would have lost his high estate. It was best.

' "Now we go on. We cannot end, as he did. It is automatic with us."

'I felt it then, somehow. The blind, purposeless continuance of the machine cities I could understand. They had no intelligence, only functions. These machines – these living, thinking, reasoning investigators – had only one function, too. Their function was slightly different – they were designed to be eternally curious, eternally investigating. And their striving was the more purposeless of the two, for theirs could reach no end. The cities fought eternally only the blind destructiveness of nature, wear, decay, erosion.

'But their struggle had an opponent forever, so long as they existed. The intelligent – no, not quite intelligent, but something else – curious machines were without opponents. They had to be curious. They had to go on investigating. And they had been going on in just this way for such incomprehensible ages that there was no longer anything to be curious about. Whoever, whatever designed them gave them wonder if there might, somewhere, be one more thing to learn.

'That – and the problem they did not want to solve, because of the blind functioning of their very structure.

'Those eternal cities were limited. The machines saw now that limit, and so the hope of final surcease in it. They worked on the energy of the atom. But the masses of the suns were yet tremendous. They were dead for want of energy. The masses of the planets were still enormous. But they, too, were dead for want of energy.

'The machines there on Neptune gave me food and drink – strange, synthetic foods and drinks. There had been none on all the planet. They, perforce, started a machine, unused in a billion years and more, that I might eat. Perhaps they were glad to do so. It brought the end appreciably nearer, that vast consumption of mine.

'They used so very, very little, for they were so perfectly efficient. The only possible fuel in all the universe is one – hydrogen. From hydrogen, the lightest of elements, the heaviest can be built up, and energy released. They knew how to destroy matter utterly to energy, and could do it.

'But while the energy release of hydrogen compounding to the heavy elements is controllable, the destruction of matter to energy is a self-regenerative process. Started once, it spreads while matter lies within its direct, contiguous reach. It is wild, uncontrollable. It is impossible to utilize the full energy of matter.

'The suns had found that. They had burned their hydrogen until it was a remnant so small the action could not go on.

'On all Earth there was not an atom of hydrogen – nor was there on any planet, save Neptune. And there the store was not great. I used an appreciable fraction while I was there. That is their last hope. They can see the end, now.

'I stayed those few days, and the machines came and went. Always investigating, always curious. But there is in all that universe nothing to investigate save the one problem they do not want to solve – the problem they are sure they cannot solve.

'The machine took me back to Earth, set up something near me that glowed with a peculiar, steady, grey light. It would fix the magnetic axis on me, on my location, within a few hours. He could not stay near when the axis touched again. He went back to Neptune, but a few millions of miles distant, in this shrunken mummy of the solar system.

'I stood alone on the roof of the city, in the frozen garden with its deceptive look of life.

'And I thought of that night I had spent, sitting up with the dead man. I had come and watched him die. And I sat up with him in the quiet. I had wanted someone, anyone to talk to.

'I did then. Overpoweringly it came to me I was sitting up in the night of the universe, in the night and quiet of the universe, with a dead planet's body, with the dead, ashen hopes of countless, nameless generations of men and women. The universe was dead, and I sat up alone – alone in the dead hush.

'Out beyond, a last flicker of life was dying on the planet Neptune – a last, false flicker of aimless life, but not life. Life was dead. The world was dead.

'I knew there would never be another sound here. For all the little remainder of time. For this was the dark and the night of time and the universe. It was inevitable, the inevitable end that had been simply more distant in my day – in the long long-gone time when the stars were mighty lighthouses of a mighty space, not the dying, flickering candles at the head of a dead planet.

'It had been inevitable then; the candles must burn out for all their brave show. But now I could see them guttering low, the last, fruitless dregs of energy escaping as the machines below had spent their last dregs of energy in that hopeless, utterly faithful gesture – to attempt the repair of the city already dead.

'The universe had been dead a billion years. It had been. This, I saw, was the last radiation of the heat of life from an already-dead body – the feel of life and warmth, imitation of life by a corpse. Those suns had long and long since ceased to generate energy. They were dead, and their corpses were giving off the last, lingering life heat before they cooled.

'I ran. I think I ran – down away from the flickering, red suns in the sky. Down to the shrouding blackness of the dead city below, where neither light, nor heat, nor life, nor imitation of life bothered me.

'The utter blackness quieted me somewhat. So I turned off my oxygen valves, because I wanted to die sane, even here, and I knew I'd never come back.

'The impossible happened! I came to with that raw oxygen in my face. I don't know how I came – only that here is warmth and life.

'Somewhere, on the far side of that bismuth coil, inevitable still, is the dead planet and the flickering, guttering candles that light the death watch I must keep at the end of time.'

NIGHT

The story contains two notions that are very common in science fiction: anti-gravity and time-travel. Both are quite impossible in the light of our present knowledge of the Universe.

According to Einstein's theory of relativity there is no way of insulating one's self from the effect of a gravitational field, nor is there such a thing as gravitational repulsion.

As for time-travel, that would seriously compromise the law of cause-and-effect, one of the fundamentals on which science is based. Breaking the law would introduce unusual paradoxes. Suppose you travelled back in time and killed your grandfather when he was still a baby. In that case you would never have been born; but if you had never been born, how could you have gone back to kill him?

Science fiction writers have written very ingenious stories to take care of such paradoxes, but orthodox science will have none of it.

Don A. Stuart, whose name is listed here as the author of this story, is, in reality, John W. Campbell, Jr., who has edited the magazine *Astounding Science Fiction* (from which more than half the stories in this book have been taken) ever since 1938.* Campbell had an excellent training in science and we can be sure he is careful about his details. He uses anti-gravity and time-travel just the same, because they give rise to such interesting plots that they must be used even when they are known to be non-scientific. (Faster-than-light travel is another item so useful to science fiction writers that its impossibility is ignored or hastily argued away.)

Stuart pictures a far-distant future, long after the Sun has 'died'. His picture of that death is of a cool Sun, barely red-hot. It appears very large in the sky, perhaps because in all the ages the Earth has crept closer to it, or perhaps because it has expanded. He does not specify.

This was reasonable at the time the story was published in 1935. Since then, however, much more has been learned of the evolution of stars. The Sun indeed is supported by the fusion of hydrogen atoms (which Campbell correctly calls the fundamental fuel of the Universe) but when its hydrogen begins to run low, other types of nuclear reactions take place. Far from cooling down, the Sun is expected to heat up with time and eventually expand greatly into a red giant. The Earth is very likely to be scorched, perhaps even vapourized at this time, which, however, will not come for another 8 billion years at least.

At one point, Campbell states that 'Earth was already, in our time, two billions of years old'. This was indeed thought to be so by astronomers in the 1930s, but geologists were sure that Earth was much older, and it turned out that the geologists were right. The Earth

* In 1960, the magazine changed its name to *Analog Science Fact-Fiction*.

has existed in solid form, it is now believed, about 4.7 billion years.

Questions and Suggestions

1. Some scientists wonder if 'anti-particles' might possess anti-gravitational forces and might therefore repel ordinary particles. What are anti-particles? Suppose you had an anti-particle and a particle near each other, could you measure the gravitational force between them and decide whether it was an attraction or a repulsion? How strong is gravitational force anyway, compared to electromagnetic force, for instance?

2. Look up information on stellar evolution and find out what is likely to happen to the Sun after the red giant stage. Some stars pass through a 'supernova' stage in the course of their development? What is a supernova and is the Sun ever likely to become one?

3. Why did astronomers think the Universe was no more than 2 billion years old in the 1930s? Why did geologists, in those days, insist the Earth was more than 2 billion years old? When and why did the astronomers change their minds and how old do they think the Universe may be nowadays? Suppose you had only the astronomical and geological information of the 1930s. Would you have believed the Universe to be young or old and why?

4. Campbell mentions the far-future Earth as having an atmosphere of helium and neon. Why those two gases? Are there any other possibilities. Campbell also mentions 'superconduction' (more often called 'superconductivity'). Look up superconductivity. What is it? At what temperatures does it exist? What is its relationship to electrical resistance? Do you think the men of the future might have built machinery that would not have been put out of order by superconductivity?

3. THE DAY IS DONE

Lester del Rey

Hwoogh scratched the hair on his stomach and watched the sun climb up over the hill. He beat listlessly on his chest and yelled at it timidly, then grumbled and stopped. In his youth, he had reared and stumped around to help the god up, but now it wasn't worth the effort. Nothing was. He found a fine flake of sweaty salt under his hair, licked it off his fingers, and turned over to sleep again.

But sleep wouldn't come. On the other side of the hill there was a hue and cry, and somebody was beating a drum in a throbbing chant. The old Neanderthaler grunted and held his hands over his ears, but the Sun-Warmer's chant couldn't be silenced. More ideas of the Talkers.

In his day, it had been a lovely world, full of hairy grumbling people; people a man could understand. There had been game on all sides, and the caves about had been filled with the smoke of cooking fires. He had played with the few young that were born – though each year fewer children had come into the tribe – and had grown to young manhood with the pride of achievement. But that was before the Talkers had made this valley one of their hunting grounds.

Old traditions, half told, half understood, spoke of the land in the days of old, when only his people roamed over the broad tundra. They had filled the caves and gone out in packs too large for any animal to withstand. And the animals swarmed into the land, driven south by the Fourth Glaciation. Then the great cold had come again, and times had been hard. Many of his people had died.

But many had lived, and with the coming of the warmer, drier climate again, they had begun to expand before the Talkers arrived. After that – Hwoogh stirred uneasily – for no good reason he could see, the Talkers took more and more of the land, and his people retreated and diminished before them. Hwoogh's father had made it understood that their little band in the valley was all that was left, and that this was the only place on the great flat earth where Talkers seldom came.

Hwoogh had been twenty when he first saw them, great long-legged men, swift of foot and eye, stalking along as if they owned the earth, with their incessant mouth noises. In the summer that year, they pitched their skin-and-wattle tents at the back of the hill, away from the caves, and made magic to their gods. There was magic on their weapons, and the beasts fell their prey. Hwoogh's people had settled back, watching fearfully, hating numbly, finally resorting to begging and stealing. Once a young buck had killed the child of a Talker, and been flayed and sent out to die for it. Thereafter, there had been a truce between Cro-Magnon and Neanderthaler.

Now the last of Hwoogh's people were gone, save only himself, leaving no children. Seven years it had been since Hwoogh's brother had curled up in the cave and sent his breath forth on the long journey to his ancestors. He had always been dispirited and weak of will, but he had had been the only friend left to Hwoogh.

The old man tossed about and wished that Keyoda would return. Maybe she would bring food from the Talkers. There was no use hunting now, when the Talkers had already been up and killed all the easy game. Better that a man should sleep all the time, for sleep was the only satisfying thing left in the topsy-turvy world; even the drink the tall Cro-Magnons made from mashed roots left a headache the next day.

He twisted and turned in his bed of leaves at the edge of the cave, grunting surlily. A fly buzzed over his head provocatively, and he lunged at it. Surprise lighted his features as his fingers closed on the insect, and he swallowed it with a momentary flash of pleasure. It wasn't as good as the grub in the forest, but it made a tasty appetizer.

The sleep god had left, and no amount of lying still and snoring would lure him back. Hwoogh gave up and squatted down on his haunches. He had been meaning to make a new head for his crude spear for weeks, and he rummaged around in the cave for materials. But the idea grew farther away the closer he approached work, and he let his eyes roam idly over the little creek below him and the fleecy clouds in the sky. It was a warm spring, and the sun made idleness pleasant.

The sun god was growing stronger again, chasing the old fog and mist away. For years, he had worshipped the sun god as his, and now it seemed to grow strong again only for the Talkers. While the god was weak, Hwoogh's people had been mighty; now that its long sickness was over, the Cro-Magnons spread out over the country like the fleas on his belly.

Hwoogh could not understand it, perhaps the god was mad at him since gods are utterly unpredictable. He grunted, wishing again for his brother who had understood such things better.

Keyoda crept around the boulder in front of the cave, interrupting his brooding. She brought scraps of food from the tent village and the half-chewed leg of a horse, which Hwoogh seized on and ripped at with his strong teeth. Evidently the Talkers had made a big kill the day before, for they were lavish with their gifts. He grunted at Keyoda, who sat under the cave entrance in the sun, rubbing her back.

Keyoda was as hideous as most of the Talkers were to Hwoogh, with her long dangling legs and short arms, and the ungainly straightness of her carriage. Hwoogh remembered the young girls of his own day with a sigh; they had been beautiful, short and squat, with forward-jutting necks and nice low foreheads. How the flat-faced Cro-Magnon women could get mates had been a puzzle to Hwoogh, but they seemed to succeed.

Keyoda had failed, however, and in her he felt justified in his judgment. There were times when he felt almost in sympathy with her, and in his own way he was fond of her. As a child, she had been injured, her back made useless for the work of a mate. Kicked around by the others of her tribe, she had gradually drifted away from them, and when she stumbled on Hwoogh, his hospitality had been welcome to her. The Talkers were nomads who followed the herds north in the summer, south in the winter, coming and going with the seasons, but Keyoda stayed with Hwoogh in his cave and did the few desultory tasks that were necessary. Even such a half-man as the Neanderthaler was preferable to the scornful pity of her own people, and Hwoogh was not unkind.

'Hwunkh?' asked Hwoogh. With his stomach partly filled, he felt more kindly towards the world.

'Oh, they come out and let me pick up their scraps – me, who was once a chief's daughter! – same as they always do.' Her voice had been shrewish, but the weariness of failure and age had taken the edge from it. ' "Poor, poor Keyoda," thinks they, "let her have what she wants, just so it don't mean nothin' we like." Here.' She handed him a roughly made spear, flaked on both sides of the point, but with only a rudimentary barb, unevenly made. 'One of 'em give me this – it ain't the like of what they'd use, I guess, but it's good as you could make. One of the kids is practising.'

Hwoogh examined it; good, he admitted, very good, and the point was fixed nicely in the shaft. Even the boys, with their long limber thumbs that could twist any which way, made better weapons than he; yet once, he had been famous among his small tribe for the nicety of his flint work.

Making a hoarse gesture, he got slowly to his feet. The shape of his jaw and the attachment of his tongue, together with a poorly developed left frontal lobe of his brain, made speech rudimentary, and he supplemented his glottals and labials with motions that Keyoda understood well enough. She shrugged and waved him out, gnawing on one of the bones.

Hwoogh wandered about without much spirit, conscious that he was growing old. And vaguely, he knew that age should not have fallen upon him for many snows; it was not the number of seasons, but something else, something that he could feel but not understand. He struck out for the hunting fields, hoping that he might find some game for himself that would require little effort to kill. The scornful gifts of the Talkers had become bitter in his mouth.

But the sun god climbed up to the top of the blue cave without Hwoogh's stumbling on anything. He swung about to return, and ran into a party of Cro-Magnons returning with the carcase of a reindeer strapped to a pole on their shoulders. They stopped to yell at him.

'No use, Hairy One!' they boasted, their voices light and gay. 'We caught all the game this way. Turn back to your cave and sleep.'

Hwoogh dropped his shoulders and veered away, his spear dragging limply on the ground. One of the party trotted over to him lightly. Sometimes Legoda, the tribal magic man and artist, seemed almost friendly, and this was one of the times.

'It was my kill, Hairy One,' he said tolerantly. 'Last night I drew strong reindeer magic, and the beast fell with my first throw. Come to my tent and I'll save a leg for you. Keyoda taught me a new song that she got from her father, and I would repay her.'

Legs, ribs, bones! Hwoogh was tired of the outer meat. His body demanded the finer food of the entrails and liver. Already his skin was itching with a rash, and he felt that he must have the succulent inner parts to make him well; always, before, that had cured him. He grunted, between appreciation and annoyance, and turned off. Legoda pulled him back.

'Nay, stay, Hairy One. Sometimes you bring good fortune to me, as when I found the bright ochre for my drawing. There is meat enough in the camp for all. Why hunt today?' As Hwoogh still hesitated, he grew more insistent, not from kindness, but more from a wish to have his own way. 'The wolves are running near today, and one is not enough against them. We carve the reindeer at the camp as soon as it comes from the poles. I'll give you first choice of the meat!'

Hwoogh grunted a surly acquiescence and waddled after the party. The dole of the Talkers had become gall to him, but liver was liver — if Legoda kept his bargain. They were chanting a rough marching song, trotting easily under the load of the reindeer, and he lumbered along behind, breathing hard at the pace they set.

As they neared the village of the nomads, its rough skin tents and burning fires threw out a pungent odour that irritated Hwoogh's nostrils. The smell of the long-limbed Cro-Magnons was bad enough without the dirty smell of a camp and the stink of their dung-fed fires. He preferred the accustomed mouldy stench of his own musty cave.

Youths came swarming out at them, yelling with disgust at being left behind on this easy hunt. Catching sight of the Neanderthaler, they set up a howl of glee and charged at him, throwing sticks and rocks and jumping at him with play fury. Hwoogh shivered and crouched over, menacing them with his spear, and giving voice to throaty growls. Legoda laughed.

'In truth, O Hairy Chokanga, your voice should drive them from you. But see, they fear it not. Kuck, you two-legged pests! Out and away! Kuck, I say!' They leaped back at his voice and dropped behind, still yelling. Hwoogh eyed them warily, but so long as it suited the pleasure of Legoda, he was safe from their pranks.

Legoda was in a good mood, laughing and joking, tossing his quips at the women until his young wife came out and silenced it. She sprang at the reindeer with her flint knife, and the other women joined her.

'Heyo,' called Legoda. 'First choice goes to Chokanga, the Hairy One. By my word, it is his.'

'Oh, fool!' There was scorn in her voice and in the look she gave Hwoogh. 'Since when do we feed the beasts of the caves and the fish of the river? Art mad, Legoda. Let him hunt for himself.'

Legoda tweaked her back with the point of his spear, grinning. 'Aye, I knew thou'dst cry at that. But then, we owe his kind some pay – this was his hunting ground when we were but pups, struggling into this far land. What harm to give to an old man?' He swung to Hwoogh and gestured. 'See, Chokanga, my word is good. Take what you want, but see that it is not more than your belly and that of Keyoda can hold this night.'

Hwoogh darted in and came out with the liver and the fine sweet fat from the entrails. With a shrill cry of rage, Legoda's mate sprang for him, but the magic man pushed her back.

'Nay, he did right! Only a fool would choose the haunch when the heart of the meat was at hand. By the gods of my father, and I expected to eat that myself! O Hairy One, you steal the meat from my mouth, and I like you for it. Go, before Heyo get free.'

Tomorrow, Hwoogh knew, Legoda might set the brats on him for this day's act, but tomorrow was in another cave of the sun. He drew his legs under him and scuttled off to the left and around the hill, while the shrill yells of Heyo and the lazy good humour of Legoda followed. A piece of liver dangled loose, and Hwoogh sucked on it as he went. Keyoda would be pleased, since she usually had to do the begging for both of them.

And a little of Hwoogh's self-respect returned. Hadn't

he outsmarted Legoda and escaped with the choicest meat? And had Keyoda ever done as well when she went to the village of the Talkers? Ayeee, they had a thing yet to learn from the cunning brain of old Hwoogh!

Of course the Talkers were crazy; only fools would act as Legoda had done. But that was none of his business. He patted the liver and fat fondly and grinned with a slight return of good humour. Hwoogh was not one to look a gift horse in the mouth.

The fire had shrunk to a red bed of coals when he reached the cave, and Keyoda was curled up on his bed, snoring loudly, her face flushed. Hwoogh smelled her breath, and his suspicions were confirmed. Somehow, she had drunk of the devil brew of the Talkers, and her sleep was dulled with its stupor. He prodded her with his toe, and she sat up bleary-eyed.

'Oh, so you're back. Ayeee, and with liver and fat! But that never came from your spear throw; you been to the village and stole it. Oh, but you'll catch it!' She grabbed at the meat greedily and stirred up the fire, spitting the liver over it.

Hwoogh explained as best he could, and she got the drift of it. 'So? Eh, that Legoda, what a prankster he is, and my own nephew, too.' She tore the liver away, half raw, and they fell to eagerly, while she chuckled and cursed by turns. Hwoogh touched her nose and wrinkled his face up.

'Well, so what if I did?' Liquor had sharpened her tongue. 'That no-good son of the chief come here, after me to be telling him stories. And to make my old tongue free, he brings me the root brew. Ah, what stories I'm telling – and some of 'em true, too!' She gestured towards a crude pot. 'I reckon he steals it, but what's that to us? Help yourself, Hairy One. It ain't ever' day we're getting the brew.'

Hwoogh remembered the headaches of former experiments, but he smelled it curiously and the lure of the magic water caught at him. It was the very essence of youth, the fire that brought life to his legs and memories to his mind. He held it up to his mouth, gasping as the beery liquid ran down his throat. Keyoda caught it before he could finish and drained the last quart.

'Ah, it strengthens my back and puts the blood a-running hot through me again.' She swayed on her feet and sputtered out the fragments of an old skin-scraping song. 'Now, there you go – can't you never learn not to drink it all at once? That way, it don't last as long and you're out before you get to feeling good.'

Hwoogh staggered as the brew took hold of him, and his knees bent even farther under him. The bed came up in his face, his head was full of bees buzzing merrily, and the cave spun around him. He reared at the cave, while Keyoda laughed.

'Heh! To hear you a-yelling, a body might think you was the only Chokanga left on earth. But you ain't – no, you ain't!'

'Hwunkh?' That struck home. To the best of Hwoogh's knowledge, there were no others of his kind left on earth. He grabbed at her and missed, but she fell and rolled against him, her breath against his face.

'So? Well, it's the truth. The kid up and told me. Legoda found three of 'em, just like you, he says, up the land to the east, three springs ago. You'll have to ask him – I dunno nothing about it.' She rolled over against him, grunting half-formed words, and he tried to think of this new information. But the brew was too strong for his head, and he was soon snoring beside her.

Keyoda was gone to the village when he awoke, and the sun was a spear length high on the horizon. He rummaged around for a piece of the liver, but the flavour was not as good as it had been, and his stomach protested lustily at going to work again. He leaned back until his head got control of itself, then swung down to the creek to quench a thirst devil that had seized on him in the night.

But there was something he should do, something he half remembered from last night. Hadn't Keyoda said something about others of his people? Yes, three of them, and Legoda knew. Hwoogh hesitated, remembering that he had bested Legoda the day before; the young man might resent it today. But he was filled with an overwhelming curiosity, and there was a strange yearning in his heart. Legoda must tell him.

Reluctantly, he went back to the cave and fished around in a hole that was a secret even from Keyoda. He drew out his treasures, fingering them reverently, and selecting the best. There were bright shells and coloured pebbles, a roughly drilled necklace that had

70

belonged to his father, a sign of completed manhood, bits of this and that with which he had intended to make himself ornaments. But the quest for knowledge was stronger than the pride of possession; he dumped them out into his fist and struck out for the village.

Keyoda was talking with the women, whining the stock formula that she had developed, and Hwoogh skirted around the camp, looking for the young artist. Finally he spotted the Talker out behind the camp, making odd motions with two sticks. He drew near cautiously, and Legoda heard him coming.

'Come near, Chokanga, and see my new magic.' The young man's voice was filled with pride, and there was no threat to it. Hwoogh sighed with relief, but sidled up slowly. 'Come nearer, don't fear me. Do you think I'm sorry of the gift I made? Nay, that was my own stupidity. See.'

He held out the sticks and Hwoogh fingered them carefully. One was long and springy, tied end to end with a leather thong, and the other was a little spear with a tuft of feather on the blunt end. He grunted a question.

'A magic spear, Hairy One, that flies from the hand with wings, and kills beyond the reach of other spears.'

Hwoogh snorted. The spear was too tiny to kill more than rodents, and the big stick had not even a point. But he watched as the young man placed the sharp stick to the tied one, and drew back on it. There was a sharp twang, and the little spear sailed out and away, burying its point in the soft bark of a tree more than two spear throws away. Hwoogh was impressed.

'Aye, Chokanga, a new magic that I learned in the south last year. There are many there who use it, and with it they can throw the point farther and better than a full-sized spear. One man may kill as much as three!'

Hwoogh grumbled; already they killed all the good game, and yet they must find new magic to increase their powers. He held out his hand curiously, and Legoda gave him the long stick and another spear, showing him how it was held. Again there was a twang, and the leather thong struck at his wrist, but the weapon sailed off erratically, missing the tree by yards. Hwoogh handed it back glumly – such magic was not

71

for his kind. His thumbs made the handling of it even more difficult.

Now, while the magic man was pleased with his superiority, was a good time to show the treasure. Hwoogh spread it out on the bare earth and gestured at Legoda, who looked down thoughtfully.

'Yes,' the Talker conceded. 'Some of it is good, and some would make nice trinkets for the women. What is it you want – more meat, or one of the new weapons? Your belly was filled yesterday; and with my beer, that was stolen, I think, though for that I blame you not. The boy has been punished already. And this weapon is not for you.'

Hwoogh snorted, wriggled and fought for expression, while the young man stared. Little by little, his wants were made known, partly by signs, partly by the questions of the Cro-Magnon. Legoda laughed.

'So, there is a call of the kind in you, Old Man?' He pushed the treasure back to Hwoogh, except one gleaming bauble. 'I would not cheat you, Chokanga, but this I take for the love I bear you, as a sign of our friendship.' His grin was mocking as he stuck the valuable in a flap of his clout.

Hwoogh squatted down on his heels, and Legoda sat on a rock as he began. 'There is but little to tell you, Hairy One. Three years ago I did run on to a family of your kind – a male and his mate, with one child. They ran from us, but we were near their cave, and they had to return. We harmed them not, and sometimes gave them food, letting them accompany us on the chase. But they were thin and scrawny, too lazy to hunt. When we returned next year, they were dead, and so far as I know, you are the last of your kind.'

He scratched his head thoughtfully. 'Your people die too easily. Chokanga; no sooner do we find them and try to help them than they cease hunting and become beggers. And then they lose interest in life, sicken and die. I think your gods must be killed off by our stronger ones.'

Hwoogh grunted a half assent, and Legoda gathered up his bow and arrows, turning back towards camp. But there was a strange look on the Neanderthaler's face that did not escape the young man's eyes. Recognizing the misery in Hwoogh's expression, he laid a hand on the old man's shoulder and spoke more kindly.

'That is why I would see to your well-being, Hairy One. When you are gone, there will be no more, and my children will laugh at me and say I lie when I spin the tale of your race at the feast fire. Each time that I kill, you shall not lack for food.'

He swung down the single street towards the tent of his family, and Hwoogh turned slowly back towards his cave. The assurance of food should have cheered him, but it only added to his gloom. Dully, he realized that Legoda treated him as a small child, or as one whom the sun god had touched with madness.

Hwoogh heard the cries and laughter of children as he rounded the hill, and for a minute he hesitated before going on. But the sense of property was well developed in him, and he leaped forward grimly. They had no business near his cave.

They were of all ages and sizes, shouting and chasing each other about in a crazy disorder. Having been forbidden to come on Hwoogh's side of the hill, and having broken the rule in a bunch, they were making the most of their revolt. Hwoogh's fire was scattered down the side of the hill into the creek, and they were busily sorting through the small store of his skins and weapons.

Hwoogh let out a savage yell and ran forward, his spear held out in jabbing position. Hearing him, they turned and jumped back from the cave entrance, clustering up into a tight group. 'Go on away, Ugly Face,' one yelled. 'Go scare the wolves! Ugly Face, Ugly Face, waaaah!'

He dashed in among them, brandishing his spear, but they darted back on their nimble legs, slipping easily from in front of him. One of the older boys thrust out a leg and caught him, tripping him down on the rocky ground. Another dashed in madly and caught his spear away, hitting him roughly with it. From the time of the first primate, the innate cruelty of thoughtlessness had changed little in children.

Hwoogh let out a whooping bellow, scrambled up clumsily and was in among them. But they slipped nimbly out of his clutching hands. The little girls were dancing around gleefully, chanting: 'Ugly Face ain't got no mother, Ugly Face ain't got no wife, waaaah on Ugly Face!' Frantically he caught at one of the boys, swung him about savagely, and tossed him on the ground, where the youth lay white and silent. Hwoogh felt a momentary glow of elation at his strength. Then somebody threw a rock.

The old Neanderthaler was tied down crudely when he swam back to consciousness, and three of the boys sat on his chest, beating the ground with their heels in time to a victory chant. There was a dull ache in his head, and bruises were swelling on his arms and chest where they had handled him roughly. He growled savagely, heaving up, and tumbled them off, but the cords were too strong for him. As surely as if grown men had done it, he was captured.

For years they had been his enemies, ever since they had found that Hwoogh-baiting was one of the pleasant occupations that might relieve the tedium of camp life. Now that the old feud was about finished, they went at the business of subduing him with method and ingenuity.

While the girls rubbed his face with soft mud from the creek, the boys ransacked the cave and tore at his clothes. The rough bag in which he had put his valuables came away in their hands, and they paused to distribute this new wealth. Hwoogh howled madly.

But a measure of sanity was returning to them, now that the first fury of the fight was over, and Kechaka, the chief's eldest son, stared at Hwoogh doubtfully. 'If the elders hear of this,' he muttered unhappily, 'there will be trouble. They'd not like our bothering Ugly Face.'

Another grinned. 'Why tell them? He isn't a man, anyway, but an animal; see the hair on his body! Toss old Ugly Face in the river, clean up his cave, and hide these treasures. Who's to know?'

There were half-hearted protests, but the thought of the beating waiting for them added weight to the idea. Kechaka nodded finally, and set them to straightening up the mess they had made. With broken branches, they eliminated the marks of their feet, leaving only the trail to the creek.

Hwoogh tossed and pitched in their arms as four of them picked him up; the bindings loosened somewhat, but not enough to free him. With some satisfaction, he noted that the boy he had caught was still retching and moaning, but that was no help to his present position. They waded relentlessly into the water, laid him on it belly down, and gave him a strong push that sent him gliding out through the rushing stream. Foaming and gasping, he fought the current, struggling against his bonds. His lungs ached for air, and the current buffeted him about; blackness was creeping up on his mind.

With a last desperate effort he tore loose the bonds and pushed up madly for the surface, gulping in air greedily. Water was unpleasant to him, but he could swim, and struck out for the bank. The children were disappearing down the trail, and were out of sight as he climbed from the water, bemoaning his lost fire that would have warmed him. He lumbered back to his cave and sank soddenly on the bed.

He, who had been a mighty warrior, bested by a snarling pack of Cro-Magnon brats! He clenched his fists savagely and growled, but there was nothing he could do. Nothing! The futility of his own effort struck down on him like a burning knife. Hwoogh was an old man, and the tears that ran from his eyes were the bitter, aching tears that only age can shed.

Keyoda returned late, cursing when she found the fire gone, but her voice softened as she spied him huddled in his bed, staring dully at the wall of the cave. Her old eyes spotted the few footprints the boys had missed, and she swore with a vigour that was almost youthful before she turned back to Hwoogh.

'Come, Hairy One, get out of that cold, wet fur!' Her hands were gentle on the straps, but Hwoogh shook her aside. 'You'll be sick, lying there on them few leaves, all wet like that. Get off the fur, and I'll go back to the village for fire. Them kids! Wait'll I tell Legoda!'

Seeing there was nothing he would let her do for him, she turned away down the trail. Hwoogh sat up to change his furs, then lay back. What was the use? He grumbled a little when Keyoda returned with fire, but refused the delicacies she had wheedled at the village, and tumbled over into a fitful sleep.

The sun was long up when he awoke to find Legoda and Keyoda fussing over him. There was an unhappy feeling in his head, and he coughed. Legoda patted his back. 'Rest, Hairy One. You have the sickness devil that burns the throat and runs the nose, but that man can overcome. Ayeee, how the boys were whipped! I, personally, attended to that, and this morning not one is less sore than you. Before they bother you again, the moon will eat up the sun.'

Keyoda pushed a stew of boiled liver and kidneys at him, but he shoved it away. Though the ache in his head had gone down, a dull weight seemed to rest on his stomach, and he could not eat. It felt as though all the boys he had fought were sitting on his chest and choking him.

Legoda drew out a small painted drum and made heavy magic for his recovery, dancing before the old man and shaking the magic gourd that drove out all sickness devils. But this was a stronger devil. Finally the young man stopped and left for the village, while Keyoda perched on a stone to watch over the sick man. Hwoogh's mind was heavy and numb, and his heart was laden in his breast. She fanned the flies away, covering his eyes with a bit of skin, singing him some song that the mothers lulled their children with.

He slept again, stirring about in a nightmare of Talker mockery, with a fever flushing his face. But when Legoda came back at night, the magic man swore he should be well in three days. 'Let him sleep and feed him. The devil will leave him soon. See, there is scarce a mark where the stone hit.'

Keyoda fed him, as best she could, forcing the food that she begged at the village down his throat. She lugged water from the creek as often as he cried for it, and bathed his head and chest when he slept. But the three days came and went, and still he was not well. The fever was little higher, and the cold little worse, than he had gone through many times before. But he did not throw it off as he should have done.

Legoda came again, bringing his magic and food, but they were of little help. As the day drew to a close, he shook his head and spoke low words to Keyoda. Hwoogh came out of a half stupor and listened dully.

'He tires of life, Keyoda, my father's sister.' The young man shrugged. 'See, he lies there not fighting. When a man will not try to live, he cannot.'

'Ayyeah!' Her voice shrilled dolefully. 'What man will not live if he can? Thou art foolish Legoda.'

'Nay. His people tire easily of life, O Keyoda. Why, I know not. But it takes little to make them die.' Seeing that Hwoogh had heard, he drew closer to the Neanderthaler. 'O Chokanga, put away your troubles, and take another bite out of life. It can still be good, if you choose. I have taken your gift as a sign of friendship, and I would keep my word. Come to my fire, and hunt no more; I will tend you as I would my father.'

Hwoogh grunted. Follow the camps, eat from Legoda's hunting, be paraded as a freak and a half-man! Legoda was kind, sudden and warm in his sympathy, but the others were scornful. And if Hwoogh should die, who was to mourn him? Keyoda would go back to her people, Legoda would forget him, and not one Chokanga would be there to show them the ritual for burial.

Hwoogh's old friends had come back to him in his dream, visiting him and showing the hunting grounds of his youth. He had heard the grunts and grumblings of the girls of his race, and they were awaiting him. That world was still empty of the Talkers, where a man could do great things and make his own kills, without hearing the laughter of the Cro-Magnons. Hwoogh sighed softly. He was tired, too tired to care what happened.

The sun sank low, and the clouds were painted a harsh red. Keyoda was wailing somewhere, far off, and Legoda beat on his drum and muttered his magic. But life was empty, barren of pride.

The sun dropped from sight, and Hwoogh sighed again, sending his last breath out to join the ghosts of his people.

THE DAY IS DONE

The first Neanderthal skeleton was discovered in 1856. It was the first indication that species of men had once existed that were more 'primitive' than the kind of man now living.

The most noticeable thing about the Neanderthal skeleton was that it had a skull with a receding forehead and a receding chin, and that there were bony ridges over the eye sockets. In these respects, it seemed midway between a gorilla and man and the notion arose that it represented an 'ape-man'.

In 1908, a French scientist, Marcellin Boule, studied a nearly complete Neanderthal skeleton and published a careful description of it. From the description, it would seem that Neanderthal man was short, just a little over five feet high. He was pictured as having such bow-legs that he had to walk on the outside part of his soles, with his knees bent. Combine that with the bony ridges, prominent teeth, receding forehead and chin, and he seemed an ugly creature indeed.

When artists drew sketches of what they thought a Neanderthal man would look like in the flesh, they were influenced by the 'ape-man' notion. They drew him with a messy stubble of hair over his face and gave him a savage, brutish expression.

Another type of man living towards the end of Neanderthal times was Cro-Magnon man. He was 'true' man, very much like ourselves; six feet in height with a straight forehead, a pronounced chin, and no bony ridges over the eyes. He was always drawn clean-shaven and was given a noble and handsome expression.

Most people supposed that Cro-Magnon man wiped out Neanderthal man quickly whenever they collided, and felt that the much superior Cro-Magnon would easily manage to slaughter the much inferior Neanderthal.

Del Rey, however, suggests something else. He supposes that while many Neanderthal men have been killed in battle with Cro-Magnon man, the crucial killing factor was the feeling of inferiority. It was this that ruined the poor 'ape-men'. They died through sheer chagrin at being outclassed even by the young adolescents of the superior species.

But was this true? It turned out eventually that the skeleton that Boule had so carefully studied was a victim of severe arthritis which had deformed the spinal column and other bones. Other Neanderthal skeletons have since been discovered which represented healthier specimens and their bones, all except those of the skull, are completely manlike. In other words, Neanderthal man didn't shamble; he walked upright just as easily and gracefully as Cro-Magnon man did.

Then, too, Neanderthal man had a large brain, just as large as that of Cro-Magnon man. To be sure, the Neanderthal brain was differently shaped. It was larger in back and smaller in front. If the front part of the brain is involved in higher-thought processes, then perhaps Neanderthal man wasn't quite as bright as Cro-Magnon, but that is by no means sure. There is certainly no real reason to think Neanderthal man couldn't talk.

In fact, nowadays, anthropologists consider both Cro-Magnon man and Neanderthal man to be the same species – *Homo sapiens*. Why did Neanderthal man die out then? Well, he didn't exactly die out. He developed into 'true' man, and those that remained of the Neanderthal variety may have interbred with the 'true' variety. In short, we are all descended from the Neanderthals in all likelihood.

Questions and Suggestions

1. Look up the details of the discovery of the first Neanderthal skeleton and the controversy that was conducted over it. What made it difficult for some people to accept the Neanderthal skeleton as a primitive kind of man?

2. When the story first appeared in *Astounding Science Fiction* the editor of the magazine (John W. Campbell, Jr.) followed it with a note to the effect that the Tasmanians, the native inhabitants of the island of Tasmania off the south-east coast of Australia, died out because of a feeling of inferiority to the incoming white man, and that the Australian aborigines were dying out for the same reason. Look up the history of Tasmania and decide for yourself why the Tasmanians died out? Are the Australian aborigines dying out now?

3. What do you think about the whole matter of 'superior' and 'inferior' varieties of man? Do you belong to a group that is superior to other groups? Or inferior? How can you tell? How does one measure such things? Look up methods of IQ testing and decide how accurately they measure intelligence when the man devising the test and the man taking the test are of different cultures.

4. How would you treat someone whom you felt was superior to you? How would you expect to be treated by him? Suppose you felt someone was inferior to him – how ought you to treat each other? What difficulties is the United States experiencing over questions such as these and how might those difficulties be resolved?

4. HEAVY PLANET

Milton A. Rothman

Ennis was completing his patrol of Sector EM, Division 426 of the Eastern Ocean. The weather had been unusually fine, the liquid-thick air roaring along in a continuous blast that propelled his craft with a rush as if it were flying, and lifting short, choppy waves that rose and fell with startling suddenness. A short savage squall whirled about, pounding down on the ocean like a million hammers, flinging the little boat ahead madly.

Ennis tore at the controls, granite-hard muscles standing out in bas-relief over his short, immensely thick body, skin gleaming scalelike in the slashing spray. The heat from the sun that hung like a huge red lantern on the horizon was a tangible intensity, making an inferno of the gale.

The little craft, that Ennis manoeuvred by sheer brawn, took a leap into the air and seemed to float for many seconds before burying its keel again in the sea. It often floated for long distances, the air was so dense. The boundary between air and water was sometimes scarcely defined at all – one merged into the other imperceptibly. The pressure did strange things.

Like a dust mote sparking in a beam, a tiny speck of light above caught Ennis's eye. A glider, he thought, but he was puzzled. Why so far out here on the ocean? They were nasty things to handle in the violent wind.

The dust mote caught the light again. It was lower, tumbling down with a precipitancy that meant trouble. An upward blast caught it, checked its fall. Then it floated down gently for a space until struck by another howling wind that seemed to distort its very outlines.

Ennis turned the prow of his boat to meet the path of the falling vessel. Curious, he thought; where were its wings? Were they retracted, or broken off? It ballooned closer, and it wasn't a glider. Far larger than any glider ever made, it was of a ridiculous shape that would not stand up for an instant. And with the sharp splash the body made as it struck the water – a splash that fell in almost the same instant it rose – a thought seemed to leap up in his mind. A thought that was more important than anything else on that planet; or was to him, at least. For if it was what he thought it was – and it had to be that – it was what Shadden had been desperately seeking for many years. What a stroke of inconceivable luck, falling from the sky before his very eyes.

The silvery shape rode the ragged waters lightly. Ennis's craft came up with a rush; he skilfully checked its speed and the two came together with a slight jar. The metal of the strange vessel dented as if it were made of rubber. Ennis stared. He put out an arm and felt the curved surface of the strange ship. His finger prodded right through the metal. What manner of people were they who made vessels of such weak materials?

He moored his little boat to the side of the larger one and climbed to an opening. The wall sagged under him. He knew he must be careful; it was frightfully weak. It would not hold together very long; he must work fast if it were to be saved. The atmospheric pressure would have flattened it out long ago, had it not been for the jagged rent above which had allowed the pressure to be equalized.

He reached the opening and lowered himself carefully into the interior of the vessel. The rent was too small; he enlarged it by taking the two edges in his hands and pulling them apart. As he went down he looked askance at the insignificant plates and beams that were like tissue paper on his world. Inside was wreckage. Nothing was left in its original shape. Crushed, mutilated machinery, shattered vacuum tubes, sagging members, all ruined by the gravity and the pressure.

There was a pulpy mess on the floor and he did not examine closely. It was like red jelly, thin and stalky, pulped under a gravity a hundred times stronger and an atmosphere ten thousand times heavier than that it had been made for.

He was in a room with many knobs and dials on the walls, apparently a control room. A table in the centre with a chart on it, the chart of a solar system. It had nine planets; his had but five.

Then he knew he was right. If they came from another system, what he wanted must be there. It could be nothing else.

He found a staircase, descended. Large machinery bulked there. There was no light, but he did not notice that. He could see well enough by infrared, and the amount of energy necessary to sustain his compact gianthood kept him constantly radiating.

Then he went through a door that was of a comfortable massiveness, even for his planet – and there it was. He recognized it at once. It was big, squat, strong. The metal was soft, but it was thick enough even to stand solidly under the enormous pull of this world. He had never seen anything quite like it. It was full of coils, magnets, and devices of shapes unknown to him. But Shadden would know. Shadden, and who knows how many other scientists before him, had tried to make something which would do what this could do, but they had all failed. And without the things this machine could perform, the race of men on Heavyplanet was doomed to stay down on the surface of the planet, chained there immovably by crushing gravity.

It was atomic energy. That he had known as soon as he knew that the body was not a glider. For nothing else but atomic energy and the fierce winds were capable of lifting a body from the surface of Heavyplanet. Chemists were impotent. There is no such thing as an explosion where the atmosphere pressed inward with more force than an explosion could press outward. Only atomic, of all the theoretically possible sources of energy, could supply the work necessary to lift a vessel away from the planet. Every other source of energy was simply too weak.

Yes, Shadden, all the scientists must see this. And quickly, because the forces of sea and storm would quickly tear the ship to shreds, and, even more vital, because the scientists of Bantin and Marak might obtain the secret if there was delay. And that would mean ruin – the loss of its age-old supremacy – for his nation. Bantin and Marak were war nations; should they obtain the secret they would use it against all the other worlds that abounded in the Universe.

The Universe was big. That was why Ennis was so sure there was atomic energy on this ship. For, even though it might have originated on a planet that was so tiny that *chemical energy* – although that was hard to visualize – would be sufficient to lift it out of the pull of gravity, to travel the distance that stretched between the stars only one thing would suffice.

He went back through the ship, trying to see what had happened.

There were pulps lying behind long tubes that pointed out through clever ports in the outer wall. He recognized them as weapons, worth looking into.

There must have been a battle. He visualized the scene. The forces that came from atomic energy must have warped even space in the vicinity. The ship pierced, the occupants killed, the controls wrecked, the vessel darting off at titanic speed, blindly into nothing. Finally it had come near enough to Heavyplanet to be enmeshed in its huge web of gravity.

Weeaao-o-ow! It was the wailing roar of his alarm siren, which brought him spinning around and dashing for his boat. Beyond, among the waves that leaped and fell so suddenly, he saw a long, low craft making way towards the derelict spaceship. He glimpsed a flash of colour on the rounded, grey superstructure, and knew it for a battleship of Marak. Luck was going strong both ways; first good, now bad. He could easily have eluded the battleship in his own small craft, but he couldn't leave the derelict. Once lost to the enemy he could never regain it, and it was too valuable to lose.

The wind howled and buffeted about his head, and he strained his muscles to keep from being blasted away as he crouched there, half on his own boat and half on the derelict. The sun had set and the evening winds were beginning to blow. The hulk scudded before them, its prow denting from the resistance of the water it pushed aside.

He thought furiously fast. With a quick motion he flipped the switch of the radiophone and called Shadden. He waited with fierce impatience until the voice of Shadden was in his ear. At last he heard it, then: 'Shadden! This is Ennis. Get your glider, Shadden, fly to a45j on my route! Quickly! It's come, Shadden! But I have no time. Come!'

He flipped the switch off, and pounded the valve out of the bottom of his craft, clutching at the side of the derelict. With a rush the ocean came up and flooded his little boat and in an instant it was gone, on its way down to the bottom. That would save him from being detected for a short time.

Back into the darkness of the spaceship. He didn't think he had been noticed climbing through the opening. Where could he hide? Should he hide? He couldn't defeat the entire battleship singlehanded, without weapons. There were no weapons that could be carried anyway. A beam of concentrated actinic light that ate away the eyes and the nervous system had to be powered by the entire output of a battleship's generators. Weapons for striking and cutting had never been developed on a world where flesh was tougher than metal. Ennis was skilled in personal combat, but how could he overcome all that would enter the derelict?

Down again, into the dark chamber where the huge atomic generator towered over his head. This time he looked for something he had missed before. He crawled around it, peering into its recesses. And then, some feet above, he saw the opening, and pulled himself up to it, carefully, not to destroy the precious thing with his mass. The opening was shielded with a heavy, darkly transparent substance through which seeped a dim glow from within. He was satisfied then. Somehow, matter was still being disintegrated in there, and energy could be drawn off if he knew how.

There were leads — wires of all sizes and busbars, and thick, heavy tubes that bent under their own weight. Some must lead in and some must lead out; it was not good to tamper with them. He chose another track. Upstairs again, and to the places where he had seen the weapons.

They were all mounted on heavy, rigid swivels. He carefully detached the tubes from the bases. The first time he tried it he was not quite careful enough, and part of the projector itself was ripped away, but next time he knew what he was doing and it came away nicely. It was a large thing, nearly as thick as his arm and twice as long. Heavy leads trailed from its lower end and a lever projected from behind. He hoped it was in working condition. He dared not try it; all he could do was to trace the leads back and make sure they were intact.

He ran out of time. There came a thud from the side, and then smaller thuds, as the boarding party incautiously leaped over. Once there was a heavy sound, as someone went all the way through the side of the ship.

'Idiots!' Ennis muttered, and moved forward with his weapon towards the stairway. Noises came from overhead, and then a loud crash buckled the plates of the ceiling. Ennis leaped out of the way, but the entire section came down, with two men on it. The floor sagged, but held for a moment. Ennis, caught beneath the downcoming mass, beat his way free. He came up with a girder in his hand, which he bent over the head of one of the Maraks. The man shook himself and struck out for Ennis, who took the blow rolling and countered with a buffet that left a black splotch on a skin that was like armour plate and sent the man through the opposite wall. The other was upon Ennis, who whirled with the quickness of one who manoeuvres habitually under a pressure of ten thousand atmospheres, and shook the Marak from him, leaving him unconscious with a twist in a sensitive spot.

The first opponent returned, and the two grappled, searching for nerve centres to beat upon. Ennis twisted frantically, conscious of the real danger that the frail vessel might break to pieces beneath his feet. The railing of a staircase gave behind the two, and they hurtled down it, crashing through the steps to the floor below. Their weight and momentum carried them through. Ennis released his grip on the Marak, stopped his fall by grasping one of the girders that was part of the ship's framework. The other continued his devastating way down, demolishing the inner shell, and then the outer shell gave way with a grinding crash that ominously became a burbling rush of liquid.

Ennis looked down into the space where the Marak had fallen, hissed with a sudden intake of breath, then dived down himself. He met rising water, gushing in through a rent in the keel. He braced himself against a girder which sagged under his hand and moved onward against the rushing water. It geysered through the hole in a heavy stream that pushed him back and started to fill the bottom level of the ship. Against that terrific pressure he strained forward slowly, beating against the resisting waves, and, with a mighty flounder, was at the opening. Its edges had been folded back upon themselves by the inrushing water, and they gaped inward like a jagged maw. He grasped them in a huge hand and exerted force. They strained for a moment and began to straighten. Irresistibly he pushed and stretched them into their former position, and then took the broken ends in his hands and *squeezed*. The metal grew soft under his grip and began to flow. The edges of the plate welded under that mighty pressure. He moved down the crack and soon it was watertight. He flexed his hands as he rose. They ached; even his strength was beginning to be taxed.

Noises from above; pounding feet. Men were coming down to investigate the commotion. He stood for a moment in thought, then turned to a blank wall, battered his way through it, and shoved the plates and girders back into position. Down to the other end of the craft, and up a staircase there. The corridor above was deserted, and he stole along it, hunting for the place he had left the weapon he had prepared. There was a commotion ahead as the Maraks found the unconscious man.

Two men came pounding up the passageway, giving him barely enough time to slip into a doorway to the side. The room he found himself in was a sleeping chamber. There were two red pulps there, and nothing that could help him, so he stayed in there only long enough to make sure that he would not be seen emerging into the hall. He crept down it again, with as little noise as possible. The racket ahead helped him: it sounded as though they were tearing the ship apart. Again he cursed their idiocy. Couldn't they see how valuable this was?

They were in the control room, ripping apart the machinery with the curiosity of children, wondering at the strange weakness of the paperlike metal, not realizing that, on the world where it was fabricated, it was sufficiently strong for any strain the builders could put upon it.

The strange weapon Ennis had prepared was on the floor of the passage, and just outside the control room. He looked anxiously at the trailing cables. Had they been stepped on and broken? Was the instrument in working condition? He had to get it and be away; no time to experiment to see if it would work.

A noise from behind, and Ennis again slunk into a doorway as a large Marak with a coloured belt around his waist strode jarringly through the corridor into the control room. Sharp orders were barked, and the men ceased their havoc with the machinery of the room. All but a few left and scattered through the ship. Ennis's face twisted into a scowl. This made things more difficult. He couldn't overcome them all single-handed, and he couldn't use the weapon inside the ship if it was what he thought it was from the size of the cables.

A Marak was standing immediately outside the room in which Ennis lurked. No exit that way. He looked around the room; there were no other doors. A port-hole in the outer wall was a tiny disc of transparency. He looked at it, felt it with his hands, and suddenly pushed his hands right through it. As quietly as he could, he worked at the edges of the circle until the hole was large enough for him to squeeze through. The jagged edges did not bother him. They felt soft, like a ragged pat of butter.

The Marak vessel was moored to the other side of the spaceship. On this side the wind howled bleakly, and the sawtooth waves stretched on and on to a horizon that was many miles distant. He cautiously made his way around the glistening rotundity of the derelict, past the prow, straining silently against the vicious backward sweep of the water that tore at every inch of his body. The darker hump of the battleship loomed up as he rounded the curve, and he swam across the tiny space to grasp a row of projections that curved up over the surface of the craft. He climbed up them, muscles that were hard as carborundum straining to hold against all the forces of gravity and wind that fought him down. Near the top of the curve was a rounded, streamlined projection. He felt around its base and found a lever there, which he moved. The metal hump slid back, revealing a rugged swivel mounting with a stubby cylindrical projector atop it.

He swung the mounting around and let loose a short, sudden blast of white fire along the naked deck of the battleship. Deep voices yelled within and men sprung out, to fall back with abrupt screams clogged in their throats as Ennis caught them in the intolerable blast from the projector. Men, shielded by five thousand miles of atmosphere from actinic light, used to receiving only red and infrared, were painfully vunerable to this frightful concentration of ultraviolet.

Noise and shouts burst from the derelict spaceship alongside, sweeping away eerily in the thundering wind that seemed to pound down upon them with new vigour in that moment. Heads appeared from the openings in the craft.

Ennis suddenly stood up to his full height, bracing himself against the wind, so dense it made him buoyant. With a deep bellow he bridged the space to the derelict. Then as a squad of Maraks made their difficult, slippery way across the flank of the battleship towards him, and as the band that had boarded the spaceship crowded out on its battered deck to see what the noise was about, he dropped down into a crouch behind his ultraviolet projector, and whirled it around, pulling the firing lever.

That was what he wanted. Make a lot of noise and disturbance, get them all on deck, and then blow them to pieces. The ravening blast spat from the nozzle of the weapon, and the men on the battleship dropped flat on the deck. He found he could not depress the projector enough to reach them. He spun it to point at the spaceship. The incandescence reached out, and then seemed to waver and die. The current was shut off at the switchboard.

Ennis rose from behind the projector, and then hurtled from the flank of the battleship as he was struck by two Maraks leaping on him from behind the hump of the vessel. The three struck the water and sank, Ennis struggling violently. He was on the last lap, and he gave all his strength to the spurt. The water swirled around them in little choppy waves that fell more quickly than the eye could follow. Heavier blows than those from an Earthly trip hammer were scoring Ennis's face and head. He was in a bad position to strike back, and suddenly he became limp and sank below the surface. The pressure of the water around him was enormous, and it increased very rapidly as he went lower and lower. He saw the shadowy bulk of the spaceship above him. His lungs were fighting for air, but he shook off his pretended stupor and swam doggedly through the water beneath the derelict. He went on and on. It seemed as though the distance were endless, following the metal curve. It was so big from beneath, and trying to swim the width without air made it bigger.

Clear, finally, his lungs drew in the saving breaths. No time to rest, though. He must make use of his advantage while it was his; it wouldn't last long. He swam along the side of the ship looking for an opening. There was none within reach from the water, so he made one, digging his stubby fingers into the metal, climbing up until it was safe to tear a rent in the thick outer and inner walls of the ship.

He found himself in one of the machine rooms of the second level. He went out into the corridor and up the stairway which was half-wrecked, and found himself in the main passage near the control room. He darted down it, into the room. There was nobody there, although the noises from above indicated that the Maraks were again descending. There was his weapon on the floor, where he had left it. He was glad that they had not got around to pulling that instrument apart. There would be one thing saved for intelligent examination.

The clatter from the descending crowd turned into a clamour of anger as they discovered him in the passageway. They stopped there for a moment, puzzled. He had been in the ocean, and had somehow magically reappeared within the derelict. It gave him time to pick up the weapon.

Ennis debated rapidly and decided to risk the unknown. How powerful the weapon was he did not know, but with atomic energy it would be powerful. He disliked using it inside the spaceship; he wanted to have enough left to float on the water until Shadden arrived; but they were beginning to advance on him, and he had to start something.

He pulled a lever. The cylinder in his arms jerked back with great force; a bolt of fierce, blinding energy tore out of it and passed with the quickness of light down the length of the corridor.

Unmindful of the heat from the object in his hands, he turned and directed it at the battleship that was plainly outlined through the space that had been once the walls of the derelict. Before the men on the deck could move, he pulled the lever again.

And the winds were silenced for a moment. The natural elements were still in fear at the incredible forces that came from the destruction of atoms. Then with an agonized scream the hurricane struck again, tore through the spot where there had been a battle-ship.

Far off in the sky Ennis detected motion. It was Shadden, speeding in a glider.

Now would come the work that was important. Shadden would take the big machine apart and see how it ran. That was what history would remember.

HEAVY PLANET

We are used to considering Earth's gravity and air pressure as so normal we are hardly aware of it. In ordinary fiction, it is never mentioned, except of course in connection with falls or storms.

In science fiction, however, such matters as gravity and air pressure are important for they vary from world to world. To be sure, we are not likely to be exposed to gravitational fields more intense or air pressures greater than those we are used to. Excluding the Sun itself, there are only four objects in the Solar system with gravitational fields more powerful than that of the Earth – these are the giant planets, Jupiter, Saturn, Uranus, and Neptune. In the foreseeable future, we are not likely to attempt landings on those planets.

These giant planets also have giant atmospheres – far denser, far deeper, involving far greater pressures at their bottoms than is true of Earth's atmosphere.

The worlds we are likely to reach will all have gravitational fields and air pressures smaller than that to which we are accustomed. The Moon has a gravitational field at its surface only one-sixth ours, and has no atmosphere at all; Mars's gravity at its surface two-fifths ours and its atmospheric pressure is no more than one-hundredth ours.

In science fiction stories, alien worlds outside our Solar system usually are very like Earth, but many stories must deal with the Moon and Mars so that low-gravitational, low-atmospheric worlds are familiar to its readers. Less familiar are pictures of conditions on Jupiter-like planets, as Heavyplanet is. Rothman labours hard to make the strange conditions on its surface come alive for us.

At the time the story was written, Milton A. Rothman was a bright college student majoring in physics, and he has since become a respected research physicist. Yet even so, he could not move ahead of the times.

The story was published in the August 1939 issue of *Astounding Science Fiction,* at which time uranium fission was on the edge of being discovered. Yet the story did not anticipate it, and it would have been unfair to expect it. No details are given of the atomic device on board the weak-walled ship from outer space (presumably from Earth). Apparently, the device releases a beam of energy that breaks down atoms that it encounters so that the author can say, 'Everything that had been in the way of the projector was gone, simply disappeared.' On the other hand it might simply mean that the great heat originating from the processes within the device vaporized everything.

And yet we must not underestimate the value of this much, either. Science fiction writers at least assumed that nuclear power could be tapped and put to work. Few scientists of the 1930s dared think so.

Questions and Suggestions
1. What is known concerning the planet Jupiter beneath the upper edge of the atmosphere – which is all we really see? What is the chemical nature of the atmosphere? How deep is it? What is its air pressure at the solid surface? What is the solid surface like? What about the other three giant planets; what are they like?
2. The story states that Heavyplanet is part of a system containing five planets altogether. The Heavyplanet being knows that, so his people had apparently developed astronomy. But suppose we imagine a race of intelligent beings on Jupiter's solid surface – what would they know about astronomy? What could they see of the heavens through Jupiter's atmosphere? What methods could be used to gain astronomical knowledge even in the absence of direct vision?
3. Venus is an unusual planet. Its surface gravity is only four-fifths that of Earth, but its atmospheric pressure at the surface is perhaps fifty times that of Earth. What do we know of conditions on Venus's surface thanks to discoveries of the 1960s? How will men manage to explore that surface?

4. Disintegrator guns were a staple of science fiction prior to the 1940s. Do you think a disintegrator gun is possible? Some people call lasers disintegrating rays because they can make things disappear in the path of their radiation. Why? How do they work? Do they disintegrate atoms?

5. '– AND HE BUILT A CROOKED HOUSE –'

Robert A. Heinlein

Americans are considered crazy anywhere in the world.

They will usually concede a basis for the accusation but point to California as the focus of the infection. Californians stoutly maintain that their bad reputation is derived solely from the acts of the inhabitants of Los Angeles County. Angelenos will, when pressed, admit the charge but explain hastily, 'It's Hollywood. It's not our fault – we didn't ask for it; Hollywood just grew.'

The people in Hollywood don't care; they glory in it. If you are interested, they will drive you up Laurel Canyon ' – where we keep the violent cases'. The Canyonites – the brown-legged women, the trunks-clad men constantly busy building and rebuilding their slap-happy unfinished houses – regard with faint contempt the dull creatures who live down in the flats, and treasure in their hearts the secret knowledge that they, and only they, know how to live.

Lookout Mountain Avenue is the name of a side canyon which twists up from Laurel Canyon. The other Canyonites don't like to have it mentioned; after all, one must draw the line somewhere!

High up on Lookout Mountain at number 8775, across the street from the Hermit – the original Hermit of Hollywood – lived Quintus Teal, graduate architect.

Even the architecture of southern California is different. Hot dogs are sold from a structure built like and designated 'The Pup'. Ice cream cones come from a giant stucco ice cream cone, and neon proclaims 'Get the Chili Bowl Habit!' from the roofs of buildings which are indisputably chili bowls. Gasoline, oil, and free road maps are dispensed beneath the wings of tri-motored transport planes, while the certified rest rooms, inspected hourly for your comfort, are located in the cabin of the plane itself. These things may surprise, or amuse, the tourist, but the local residents, who walk bareheaded in the famous California noonday sun, take them as a matter of course.

Quintus Teal regarded the efforts of his colleagues in architecture as faint-hearted, fumbling, and timid.

'What is a house?' Teal demanded of his friend, Homer Bailey.

'Well — ' Bailey admitted cautiously, 'speaking in broad terms, I've always regarded a house as a gadget to keep off the rain.'

'Nuts! You're as bad as the rest of them.'

'I didn't say the definition was complete—'

'Complete! It isn't even in the right direction. From that point of view we might just as well be squatting in caves. But I don't blame you,' Teal went on magnanimously, 'you're no worse than the lugs you find practising architecture. Even the Moderns — all they've done is to abandon the Wedding Cake School in favour of the Service Station School, chucked away the gingerbread and slapped on some chromium, but at heart they are as conservative and traditional as a county courthouse. Neutra! Schindler! What have those bums got? What's Frank Lloyd Wright got that I haven't got?'

'Commissions,' his friend answered succinctly.

'Huh- Wha' d'ju say?' Teal stumbled slightly in his flow of words, did a slight double take, and recovered himself. 'Commissions. Correct. And why? Because I don't think of a house as an upholstered cave; I think of it as a machine for living, a vital process, a live dynamic thing, changing with the mood of the dweller — not a dead, static, oversized coffin. Why should we be held down by the frozen concepts of our ancestors? Any fool with a little smattering of descriptive geometry can design a house in the ordinary way. Is the static geometry of Euclid the only mathematics? Are we to completely disregard the Picard-Vessiot theory? How about modular systems? — to say nothing of the rich suggestions of stereochemistry. Isn't there a place in architecture for transformation, for homomorphology, for actional structures?'

'Blessed if I know,' answered Bailey. 'You might just as well be talking about the fourth dimension for all it means to me.'

'And why not? Why should we limit ourselves to the — Say!' He interrupted himself and stared into distances. 'Homer, I think you've really got something.

After all, why not? Think of the infinite richness of articulation and relationship in four dimensions. What a house, what a house – ' He stood quite still, his pale bulging eyes blinking thoughtfully.

Bailey reached up and shook his arm. 'Snap out of it. What the hell are you talking about, four dimensions? Time is the fourth dimension; you can't drive nails into *that.*'

Teal shrugged him off. 'Sure. Sure. Time is *a* fourth dimension, but I'm thinking about a fourth spatial dimension, like length, breadth and thickness. For economy of materials and convenience of arrangement you couldn't beat it. To say nothing of the saving of ground space – you could put an eight-room house on the land now occupied by a one-room house. Like a tesseract—'

'What's a tesseract?'

'Didn't you go to school? A tesseract is a hypercube, a square figure with four dimensions to it, like a cube has three, and a square has two. Here, I'll show you.' Teal dashed out into the kitchen of his apartment and returned with a box of toothpicks which he spilled on the table between them, brushing glasses and a nearly empty Holland gin bottle carelessly aside. 'I'll need some plasticine. I had some around here last week.' He burrowed into a drawer of the littered desk which crowded one corner of his dining room and emerged with a lump of oily sculptor's clay. 'Here's some.'

'What are you going to do?'

'I'll show you.' Teal rapidly pinched off small masses of the clay and rolled them into pea-sized balls. He stuck toothpicks into four of these and hooked them together into a square. 'There! That's a square.'

'Obviously.'

'Another one like it, four more toothpicks, and we make a cube.' The toothpicks were now arranged in the framework of a square box, a cube, with the pellets of clay holding the corners together. 'Now we make another cube just like the first one, and the two of them will be two sides of the tesseract.'

Bailey started to help him roll the little balls of clay for the second cube, but became diverted by the sensuous feel of the docile clay and started working and shaping it with his fingers.

'Look,' he said, holding up his effort, a tiny figurine, 'Gypsy Rose Lee.'

'Looks more like Gargantua; she ought to sue you. Now pay attention. You open up one corner of the first cube, interlock the second cube at one corner, and then close the corner. Then take eight more toothpicks and join the bottom of the first cube to the bottom of the second, on a slant, and the top of the first to the top of the second, the same way.' This he did rapidly, while he talked.

'What's that supposed to be?' Bailey demanded suspiciously.

'That's a tesseract, eight cubes forming the sides of a hypercube in four dimensions.'

'It looks more like a cat's cradle to me. You're only got two cubes there anyhow. Where are the other six?'

'Use your imagination, man. Consider the top of the first cube in relation to the top of the second; that's cube number three. Then the two bottom squares, then the front faces of each cube, the back faces, the right hand, the left hand – eight cubes.' He pointed them out.

'Yeah, I see 'em. But they still aren't cubes; they're whatchamucallems – prisms. They are not square, they slant.'

'That's just the way you look at it, in perspective. If you drew a picture of a cube on a piece of paper, the side squares would be slantwise, wouldn't they? That's perspective. When you look at a four-dimensional figure in three dimensions, naturally it looks crooked. But those are all cubes just the same.'

'Maybe they are to you, brother, but they still look crooked to me.'

Teal ignored the objections and went on. 'Now consider this as the framework of an eight-room house; there's one room on the ground floor – that's for service, utilities, and garage. There are six rooms opening off it on the next floor, living room, dining room, bath, bedrooms, and so forth. And up at the top, completely enclosed and with windows on four sides, is your study. There! How do you like it?'

'Seems to me you have the bathtub hanging out of the living room ceiling. Those rooms are interlaced like an octopus.'

'Only in perspective, only in perspective. Here, I'll do it another way so you can see it.' This time Teal made a cube of toothpicks, then made a second of halves of toothpicks, and set it exactly in the centre of the first by attaching the corners of the small cube to the large cube by short lengths of toothpick. 'Now – the big cube is your ground floor, the little cube inside is your study on the top floor. The six cubes joining them are the living rooms. See?'

Bailey studied the figure, then shook his head. 'I still don't see but two cubes, a big one and a little one. Those other six things, they look like pyramids this time instead of prisms, but they still aren't cubes.'

'Certainly, certainly, you are seeing them in different perspective. Can't you see that?'

'Well, maybe. But that room on the inside, there. It's completely surrounded by the thingamujigs. I thought you said it had windows on four sides.'

'It has – it just looks like it was surrounded. That's the grand feature about a tesseract house, complete outside exposure for every room, yet every wall serves two rooms and an eight-room house requires only a one-room foundation. It's revolutionary.'

'That's putting it mildly. You're crazy, bud; you can't build a house like that. That inside room is on the inside, and there she stays.'

Teal looked at his friend in controlled exasperation. 'It's guys like you that keep architecture in its infancy. How many square sides has a cube?'

'Six.'

'How many of them are inside?'

'Why, none of 'em. They're all on the outside.'

'All right. Now listen – a tesseract has eight cubical sides, *all on the outside*. Now watch me. I'm going to open up this tesseract like you can open up a cubicle pasteboard box, until it's flat. That way you'll be able to see all eight of the cubes.' Working very rapidly he constructed four cubes, piling one on top of the other in an unsteady tower. He then built out four more cubes from the four exposed faces of the second cube in the pile. The structure swayed a little under the loose coupling of the clay pellets, but it stood, eight cubes in an inverted cross, a double cross, as the four additional cubes stuck out in four directions. 'Do you see it now? It rests on the ground floor room, the next six cubes are the living rooms, and there is your study, up at the top.'

Bailey regarded it with more approval than he had the other figures. 'At least I can understand it. You say that is a tesseract, too?'

'That is a tesseract unfolded in three dimensions. To put it back together you tuck the top cube on to the bottom cube, fold those side cubes in till they meet the top cube and there you are. You do all this folding through a fourth dimension of course; you don't distort any of the cubes, or fold them into each other.'

Bailey studied the wobbly framework further. 'Look here,' he said at last, 'why don't you forget about folding this thing up through a fourth dimension – you can't anyway – and build a house like this?'

'What do you mean, I can't? It's a simple mathematical problem—'

'Take it easy, son. It may be simple in mathematics, but you could never get your plans approved for construction. There isn't any fourth dimension; forget it. But this kind of a house – it might have some advantages.'

Checked, Teal studied the model. 'Hm-m-m— Maybe you got something. We could have the same number of rooms, and we'd save the same amount of ground space. Yes, and we would set that middle cross-shaped floor northeast, southwest, and so forth, so that every room would get sunlight all day long. That central axis lends itself nicely to central heating. We'll put the dining room on the northwest and the kitchen on the southeast, with big view windows in every room. O.K., Homer, I'll do it! Where do you want it built?'

'Wait a minute! Wait a minute! I didn't say you were going to build it for me—'

'Of course I am. Who else? Your wife wants a new house; this is it.'

'But Mrs. Bailey wants a Georgian house—'

'Just an idea she has. Women don't know what they want—'

'Mrs. Bailey does.'

'Just some idea an out-of-date architect has put in her head. She drives a 1941 car, doesn't she? She wears the very latest styles – why should she live in an eighteenth-century house? This house will be even later than a 1941 model; it's years in the future. She'll be the talk of the town.'

'Well – I'll have to talk to her.'

'Nothing of the sort. We'll surprise her with it. Have another drink.'

'Anyhow, we can't do anything about it now. Mrs. Bailey and I are driving up to Bakersfield tomorrow. The company's bringing in a couple of wells tomorrow.'

'Nonsense. That's just the opportunity we want. It will be a surprise for her when you get back. You can just write me a cheque right now, and your worries are over.'

'I oughtn't to do anything like this without consulting her. She won't like it.'

'Say, who wears the pants in your family anyhow?'

The cheque was signed about halfway down the second bottle.

Things are done fast in southern California. Ordinary houses there are usually built in a month's time. Under Teal's impassioned heckling the tesseract house climbed dizzily skywards in days rather than weeks, and its cross-shaped second storey came jutting out at the four corners of the world. He had some trouble at first with the inspectors over these four projecting rooms but by using strong girders and folding money he had been able to convince them of the soundness of his engineering.

By arrangement, Teal drove up in front of the Bailey residence the morning after their return to town. He improvised on his two-tone horn. Bailey stuck his head out of the front door. 'Why don't you use the bell?'

'Too slow,' answered Teal cheerfully. 'I'm a man of action. Is Mrs. Bailey ready? Ah, there you are, Mrs. Bailey! Welcome home, welcome home. Jump in, we've got a surprise for you!'

'You know Teal, my dear,' Bailey put in uncomfortably.

Mrs. Bailey sniffed. 'I know him. We'll go in our own car, Homer.'

'Certainly, my dear.'

'Good idea,' Teal agreed; ''sgot more power than mine; we'll get there faster. I'll drive, I know the way.' He took the keys from Bailey, slid into the driver's seat, and had the engine started before Mrs. Bailey could rally her forces.

'Never have to worry about my driving,' he assured Mrs. Bailey, turning his head as he did so, while he shot the powerful car down the avenue and swung on to Sunset Boulevard, 'it's a matter of power and control, a dynamic process, just my meat — I've never had a serious accident.'

'You won't have but one,' she said bitingly. 'Will you *please* keep your eyes on the traffic?'

He attempted to explain to her that a traffic situation was a matter, not of eyesight, but intuitive integration of courses, speeds, and probabilities, but Bailey cut him short. 'Where is the house, Quintus?'

'House?' asked Mrs. Bailey' suspiciously. 'What's this about a house, Homer? Have you been up to something without telling me?'

Teal cut in with his best diplomatic manner. 'It's certainly is a house, Mrs. Bailey. And what a house? It's a surprise for you from a devoted husband. Just wait till you see it—'

'I shall,' she agreed grimly. 'What style is it?'

'This house sets a new style. It's later than television, newer than next week. It must be seen to be appreciated. By the way,' he went on rapidly, heading off any retort, 'did you folks feel the earthquake last night?'

'Just a little one,' Teal continued, 'about two a.m. If I hadn't been awake, I wouldn't have noticed it.'

Mrs. Bailey shuddered. 'Oh, this awful country! Do you hear that, Homer? We might have been killed in our beds and never have known it. Why did I ever let you persuade me to leave Iowa?'

'But my dear,' he protested hopelessly, 'you wanted to come out to California; you didn't like Des Moines.'

'We needn't go into that,' she said firmly. 'You are a man; you should anticipate such things. Earthquakes!'

'That's one thing you needn't fear in your new home, Mrs. Bailey,' Teal told her, 'It's absolutely earthquake-proof; every part is in perfect dynamic balance with every other part.'

'Well, I hope so. Where is this house?'

'Just around this bend. There's the sign now.' A large arrow sign, of the sort favoured by real estate promoters, proclaimed in letters that were large and bright even for southern California:

THE HOUSE OF THE FUTURE! ! !

COLOSSAL — AMAZING —
REVOLUTIONARY

SEE HOW YOUR GRANDCHILDREN
WILL LIVE

Q. Teal, Architect

'Of course that will be taken down,' he added hastily, noting her expression, 'as soon as you take possession.' He slued around the corner and brought the car to a squealing halt in front of the House of the Future. *'Voilà!'* He watched their faces for response.

Bailey stared unbelievingly, Mrs. Bailey in open dislike. They saw a simple cubicle mass, possessing doors and windows, but no other architectural features, save that it was decorated in intricate mathematical designs. 'Teal,' Bailey asked slowly, 'what have you been up to?'

Teal turned from their faces to the house. Gone was the crazy tower with its jutting second-storey rooms. No trace remained of the seven rooms above ground floor level. Nothing remained but the single room that rested on the foundations. 'Great jumping cats!' he yelled, 'I've been robbed!'

He broke into a run.

But it did him no good. Front or back, the story was the same: the other seven rooms had disappeared, vanished completely. Bailey caught up with him, and took his arm. 'Explain yourself. What is this about being robbed? How come you built anything like this — it is not according to agreement.'

'But I didn't. I built just what we had planned to build, an eight-room house in the form of a developed tesseract. I've been sabotaged; that's what it is! Jealousy! The other architects in town didn't dare let me finish this job; they knew they'd be washed up if I did.'

'When were you last here?'

'Yesterday afternoon.'

'Everything all right then?'

'Yes. The gardeners were just finishing up.'

Bailey glanced around at the faultlessly manicured

landscaping. 'I don't see how seven rooms could have been dismantled and carted away from here in a single night without wrecking this garden.'

Teal looked around, too. 'It doesn't look it. I don't understand it.'

Mrs. Bailey joined them. 'Well? Well? Am I to be left to amuse myself? We might as well look it over as long as we are here, though I'm warning you, Homer, I'm not going to like it.'

'We might as well,' agreed Teal, and drew a key from his pocket with which he let them in the front door. 'We may pick up some clues.'

The entrance hall was in perfect order, the sliding screens that separated it from the garage space were back, permitting them to see the entire compartment. 'This looks all right,' observed Bailey. 'Let's go up on the roof and try to figure out what happened. Where's the staircase? Have they stolen that, too?'

'Oh, no,' Teal denied, 'look—' He pressed a button below the light switch; a panel in the ceiling fell away and a light, graceful flight of stairs swung noiselessly down. Its strength members were the frosty silver of duralumin, its treads and risers transparent plastic. Teal wriggled like a boy who has successfully performed a card trick, while Mrs. Bailey thawed perceptibly.

It was beautiful.

'Pretty slick,' Bailey admitted. 'Howsomever it doesn't seem to go any place—'

'Oh, that – ' Teal followed his gaze. 'The cover lifts up as you approach the top. Open stair wells are anachronisms. Come on.' As predicted, the lid of the staircase got out of their way as they climbed the flight and permitted them to debouch at the top, but not, as they had expected, on the roof of the single room. They found themselves standing in the middle one of the five rooms which consisted the second floor of the original structure.

For the first time on record Teal had nothing to say. Bailey echoed him, chewing on his cigar. Everything was in perfect order. Before them, through open doorway and translucent partition lay the kitchen, a chef's dream of up-to-the-minute domestic engineering monel metal, continuous counter space, concealed lighting, functional arrangement. On the left the formal, yet gracious and hospitable dining room awaited guests, its furniture in parade-ground alignment.

Teal knew before he turned his head that the drawing room and lounge would be found in equally substantial and impossible existence.

'Well, I must admit this *is* charming,' Mrs. Bailey approved, 'and the kitchen is just *too* quaint for words – though I would never have guessed from the exterior that this house had so much room upstairs. Of course *some* changes will have to be made. That secretary now – if we moved it over *here* and put the settle over *there*—'

'Stow it, Matilda,' Bailey cut in brusquely. 'Wha'd yuh make of it, Teal?'

'Why, Homer Bailey! The very id—'

'Stow it, I said. Well, Teal?'

The architect shuffled his rambling body. 'I'm afraid to say. Let's go on up.'

'How?'

'Like this.' He touched another button; a mate, in deeper colours, to the fairy bridge that had let them up from below offered them access to the next floor. They climbed it, Mrs. Bailey expostulating in the rear, and found themselves in the master bedroom. Its shades were drawn, as had been those on the level below, but the mellow lighting came on automatically. Teal at once activated the switch which controlled still another flight of stairs, and they hurried up into the top floor study.

'Look, Teal,' suggested Bailey when he had caught his breath, 'can we get to the roof above this room? Then we can look around.'

'Sure, it's an observatory platform.' They climbed a fourth flight of stairs, but when the cover at the top lifted to let them reach the level above, they found themselves, not on the roof, but *standing in the ground floor room where they had entered the house.*

Mr. Bailey turned a sickly grey. 'Angels in heaven,' he cried, 'this place is haunted. We're getting out of here.' Grabbing his wife he threw open the front door and plunged out.

Teal was too much preoccupied to bother with their departure. There was an answer to all this, an answer that he did not believe. But he was forced to break off considering it because of hoarse shouts from somewhere above him. He lowered the staircase and rushed upstairs. Bailey was in the central room over Mrs. Bailey, who had fainted. Teal took in the situation, went to the bar built into the lounge, and poured three fingers of brandy, which he returned with and handed to Bailey. 'Here – this'll fix her up.'

Bailey drank it.

'That was for Mrs. Bailey,' said Teal.

'Don't quibble,' snapped Bailey. 'Get her another.' Teal took the precaution of taking one himself before returning with a dose earmarked for his client's wife. He found her just opening her eyes.

'Here, Mrs. Bailey,' he soothed, 'this will make you feel better.'

'I never touch spirits,' she protested, and gulped it.

'Now tell me what happened,' suggested Teal. 'I thought you two had left.'

'But we did – we walked out the front door and found ourselves up here, in the lounge.'

'The hell you say! Hm-m-m – wait a minute.' Teal went into the lounge. There he found that the big view window at the end of the room was open. He peered cautiously through it. He stared, not out at the California countryside, but into the ground floor room – or a reasonable facsimile thereof. He said nothing, but went back to the stair well which he had left open and looked down it. The ground floor room was still in place. Somehow, it managed to be in two different places at once, on different levels.

He came back into the central room and seated himself opposite Bailey in a deep chair, and sighted him past his upthrust bony knees. 'Homer,' he said impressively, 'do you know what has happened?'

'No, I don't – but if I don't find out pretty soon, something is going to happen and pretty drastic, too!'

'Homer, this is a vindication of my theories. This house is a real tesseract.'

'What's he talking about, Homer?'

'Wait, Matilda – now Teal, that's ridiculous. You've pulled some hanky-panky here and I won't have it – scaring Mrs. Bailey half to death, and making me nervous. All I want is to get out of here, with no more of your trapdoors and silly practical jokes.'

'Speak for yourself, Homer,' Mrs. Bailey interrupted,

'I was *not* frightened; I was just took all over queer for a moment. It's my heart; all of my people are delicate and highstrung. Now about this tessy thing — explain yourself, Mr. Teal. Speak up.'

He told her as well as he could in the face of numerous interruptions the theory back of the house. 'Now as I see it, Mrs. Bailey,' he concluded, 'this house, while perfectly stable in three dimensions, was not stable in four dimensions. I had built a house in the shape of an unfolded tesseract; something happened to it, some jar or side thrust, and it collapsed into its normal shape — it folded up.' He snapped his fingers suddenly. 'I've got it! The earthquake!'

'Earthquake?'

'Yes, yes, the little shake we had last night. From a four-dimensional standpoint this house was like a plane balanced on edge. One little push and it fell over, collapsed along its natural joints into a stable four-dimensional figure.'

'I thought you boasted about how safe this house was.'

'It *is safe* — three-dimensionally.'

'I don't call a house safe,' commented Bailey edgily, 'that collapses at the first little tremblor.'

'But look around you, man!' Teal protested. 'Nothing has been disturbed, not a piece of glassware cracked. Rotation through a fourth dimension can't affect a three-dimensional figure any more than you can shake letters off a printed page. If you had been sleeping in here last night, you would never have awakened.'

'That's just what I'm afraid of. Incidentally, has your great genius figured out any way for us to get out of this booby trap?'

'Huh? Oh, yes, you and Mrs. Bailey started to leave and landed back up here, didn't you? But I'm sure there is no real difficulty — we came in, we can go out. I'll try it.' He was up and hurrying downstairs before he had finished talking. He flung open the front door, stepped through, and found himself staring at his companions, down the length of the second floor lounge. 'Well, there does seem to be some slight problem,' he admitted blandly. 'A mere technicality, though — we can always go out a window.' He jerked aside the long drapes that covered the deep French windows set in one side wall of the lounge. He stopped suddenly.

'Hm-m-m,' he said, 'this is interesting – very.'

'What is?' asked Bailey, joining him.

'This.' The window stared directly into the dining room, instead of looking outdoors. Bailey stepped back to the corner where the lounge and the dining room joined the central room at ninety degrees.

'But that can't be,' he protested, 'that window is maybe fifteen, twenty feet from the dining room.'

'Not in a tesseract,' corrected Teal. 'Watch.' He opened the window and stepped through, talking back over his shoulder as he did so.

From the point of view of the Baileys he simply disappeared.

But not from his own viewpoint. It took him some seconds to catch his breath. Then he cautiously disentangled himself from the rosebush to which he had become almost irrevocably wedded, making a mental note the while never again to order landscaping which involved plants with thorns, and looked around him.

He was outside the house. The massive bulk of the ground floor room thrust up beside him. Apparently he had fallen off the roof.

He dashed around the corner of the house, flung open the front door and hurried up the stairs. 'Homer!' he called out, 'Mrs. Bailey! I've found a way out!'

Bailey looked annoyed rather than pleased to see him. 'What happened to you?'

'I fell out. I've been outside the house. You can do it just as easily – just step through those French windows. Mind the rosebush, though – we may have to build another stairway.'

'How did you get back in?'

'Through the front door.'

'Then we shall leave the same way. Come, my dear.' Bailey set his hat firmly on his head and marched down the stairs, his wife on his arm.

Teal met them in the lounge. 'I could have told you that wouldn't work,' he announced. 'Now here's what we have to do: as I see it, in a four-dimensional figure a three-dimensional man has two choices every time he crosses a line of puncture, like a wall or a threshold. Ordinarily he will make a ninety-degree turn through the fourth dimension, only he doesn't feel it with his three dimensions. Look.' He stepped through the very window that he had fallen out of a moment before.

Stepped through and arrived in the dining room, where he stood, still talking.

'I watched where I was going and arrived where I intended to.' He stepped back into the lounge. 'The time before I didn't watch and I moved on through normal space and fell out of the house. It must be a matter of subconscious orientation.'

'I'd hate to depend on subconscious orientation when I step out for the morning paper.'

'You won't have to; it'll become automatic. Now to get out of the house this time— Mrs. Bailey, if you will stand here with your back to the window, and jump backward, I'm pretty sure you will land in the garden.'

Mrs. Bailey's face expressed her opinion of Teal and his ideas. 'Homer Bailey,' she said shrilly, 'are you going to stand there and let him suggest such—'

'But Mrs. Bailey,' Teal attempted to explain, 'we can tie a rope on you and lower you down eas—'

'Forget it, Teal,' Bailey cut him off brusquely. 'We'll have to find a better way than that. Neither Mrs. Bailey nor I are fitted for jumping.'

Teal was temporarily nonplussed; there ensued a short silence. Bailey broke it with, 'Did you hear that, Teal?'

'Hear what?'

'Someone talking off in the distance. D'you s'pose there could be someone else in the house, playing tricks on us, maybe?'

'Oh, not a chance. I've got the only key.'

'But I'm sure of it,' Mrs. Bailey confirmed. 'I've heard them ever since we came in. Voices. Homer, I can't stand much more of this. Do something.'

'Now, now, Mrs. Bailey,' Teal soothed, 'don't get upset. There can't be anyone else in the house, but I'll explore and make sure. Homer, you stay here with Mrs. Bailey and keep an eye on the rooms on this floor.' He passed from the lounge into the ground floor room and from there to the kitchen and on into the bedroom. This led him back to the lounge by a straight-line route, that is to say, by going straight ahead on the entire trip he returned to the place from which he started.

'Nobody around,' he reported. 'I opened all of the doors and windows as I went – all except this one.' He stepped to the window opposite the one through which he had recently fallen and thrust back the drapes.

He saw a man with his back towards him, four rooms away. Teal snatched open the French window and dived through it, shouting. 'There he goes now! Stop thief!'

The figure evidently heard him; it fled precipitately. Teal pursued, his gangling limbs stirred to unanimous activity, through drawing room, kitchen, dining room, lounge – room after room, yet in spite of Teal's best efforts he could not seem to cut down the four-room lead that the interloper had started with.

He saw the pursued jump awkwardly but actively over the low sill of a French window and in so doing knock off his hat. When he came up to the point where his quarry had lost his headgear, he stopped and picked it up, glad of an excuse to stop and catch his breath. He was back in the lounge.

'I guess he got away from me,' he admitted. 'Anyhow, here's his hat. Maybe we can identify him.'

Bailey took the hat, looked at it, then snorted, and slapped it on Teal's head. It fitted perfectly. Teal looked puzzled, took the hat off, and examined it. On the sweat band were the initials 'Q.T.' It was his own.

Slowly comprehension filtered through Teal's features. He went back to the French window and gazed down the series of rooms through which he had pursued the mysterious stranger. They saw him wave his arms sema-phore fashion. 'What are you doing?' asked Bailey.

'Come see.' The two joined him and followed his stare with their own. Four rooms away they saw the backs of three figures, two male and one female. The taller, thinner of the men was waving his arms in a silly fashion.

Mrs. Bailey screamed and fainted again.

Some minutes later, when Mrs. Bailey had been re-suscitated and somewhat composed, Bailey and Teal took stock. 'Teal,' said Bailey, 'I won't waste any time blaming you; recriminations are useless and I'm sure you didn't plan for this to happen, but I suppose you realize we are in a pretty serious predicament. How are we going to get out of here? It looks now as if we would stay until we starve; every room leads into another room.'

'Oh, it's not that bad. I got out once, you know.'

'Yes, but you can't repeat it – you tried.'

'Anyhow we haven't tried all the rooms. There's still the study.'

'Oh, yes, the study. We went through there when we first came in, and didn't stop. Is it your idea that we might get out through its windows?'

'Don't get your hopes up. Mathematically, it ought to look into the four side rooms on this floor. Still we never opened the blinds; maybe we ought to look.'

' 'Twon't do any harm anyhow. Dear, I think you had best just stay here and rest—'

'Be left alone in this horrible place? I should say not!' Mrs. Bailey was up off the couch where she had been recuperating even as she spoke.

They went upstairs. 'This is the inside room, isn't it, Teal?' Bailey inquired as they passed through the master bedroom and climbed on up towards the study. 'I mean it was the little cube in your diagram that was in the middle of the big cube, and completely surrounded.'

'That's right,' agreed Teal. 'Well, let's have a look. I figure this window ought to give into the kitchen.' He grasped the cords of Venetian blinds and pulled them.

It did not. Waves of vertigo shook them. Involuntarily they fell to the floor and grasped helplessly at the pattern on the rug to keep from falling. 'Close it! Close it!' moaned Bailey.

Mastering in part a primitive atavistic fear, Teal worked his way back to the window and managed to release the screen. The window had looked *down* instead of *out*, down from a terrifying height.

Mrs. Bailey had fainted again.

Teal went back after more brandy while Bailey chafed her wrists. When she had recovered, Teal went cautiously to the window and raised the screen a crack. Bracing his knees, he studied the scene. He turned to Bailey. 'Come look at this, Homer. See if you recognize it.'

'You stay away from there, Homer Bailey!'

'Now, Matilda, I'll be careful.' Bailey joined him and peered out.

'See up there? That's the Chrysler Building, sure as shooting. And there's the East River, and Brooklyn.' They gazed straight down the sheer face of an enormously tall building. More than a thousand feet away a toy city, very much alive, was spread out before them. 'As near as I can figure it out, we are looking down the side of the Empire State Building from a point just above its tower.'

'What is it? A mirage?'

'I don't think so – it's too perfect. I think space is folded over through the fourth dimension here and we are looking past the fold.'

'You mean we aren't really seeing it?'

'No, we're seeing it all right. I don't know what would happen if we climbed out of this window, but I for one don't want to try. But what a view! Oh, boy, what a view! Let's try the other windows.'

They approached the next window more cautiously, and it was well that they did, for it was even more disconcerting, more reason-shaking, than the one looking down the gasping height of the skyscraper. It was a simple seascape, open ocean and blue sky – but the ocean was where the sky should have been, and contrariwise. This time they were somewhat braced for it, but they felt seasickness about to overcome them at the sight of waves rolling overhead; they lowered the blind quickly without giving Mrs. Bailey a chance to be disturbed by it.

Teal looked at the third window. 'Game to try it, Homer?'

'Hrrumph – well, we won't be satisfied if we don't. Take it easy.' Teal lifted the blind a few inches. He saw nothing, and raised it a little more – still nothing. Slowly he raised it until the window was fully exposed. They gazed out at – nothing.

Nothing, nothing at all. What colour is nothing? Don't be silly! What shape is it? Shape is an attribute of *something*. It had neither depth nor form. It had not even blackness. It was *nothing*.

Bailey chewed at his cigar. 'Teal, what do you make of that?'

Teal's insouciance was shaken for the first time. 'I don't know, Homer, I don't rightly know – but I think that window ought to be walled up.' He stared at the lowered blind for a moment. 'I think maybe we looked at a place where space *isn't*. We looked around a fourth-dimensional corner and there wasn't anything here.' He rubbed his eyes. 'I've got a headache.'

They waited for a while before tackling the fourth window. Like an unopened letter, it might *not* contain

110

bad news. The doubt left him. Finally the suspense stretched too thin and Bailey pulled the cord himself, in the face of his wife's protests.

It was not so bad. A landscape stretched away from them, right side up, and on such a level that the study appeared to be a ground floor room. But it was distinctly unfriendly.

A hot, hot sun beat down from lemon-coloured sky. The flat ground seemed burned a sterile, bleached brown and incapable of supporting life. Life there was, strange stunted trees that lifted knotted, twisted arms to the sky. Little clumps of spiky leaves grew on the outer extremities of these misshapen growths.

'Heavenly day,' breathed Bailey, 'where is that?'

Teal shook his head, his eyes troubled. 'It beats me.'

'It doesn't look like anything on Earth. It looks more like another planet – Mars, maybe.'

'I wouldn't know. But, do you know, Homer, it might be worse than that, worse than another planet, I mean.'

'Huh? What's that you say?'

'It might be clear out of our space entirely. I'm not sure that that is our Sun at all. It seems too bright.'

Mrs. Bailey had somewhat timidly joined them and now gazed out at the outré scene. 'Homer,' she said in a subdued voice, 'those hideous trees – they frighten me.'

He patted her hand.

Teal fumbled with the window catch.

'What are you doing?' Bailey demanded.

'I thought if I stuck my head out the window I might be able to look around and tell a bit more.'

'Well – all right,' Bailey grudged, 'but be careful.'

'I will.' He opened the window a crack and sniffed. 'The air is all right, at least.' He threw it open wide.

His attention was diverted before he could carry out his plan. An uneasy tremor, like the first intimation of nausea, shivered the entire building for a long second, and was gone.

'Earthquake!' They all said it at once. Mrs. Bailey flung her arms around her husband's neck.

Teal gulped and recovered himself, saying:

'It's all right, Mrs. Bailey. This house is perfectly safe. You know you can expect settling tremors after a shock like last night.' He had just settled his features into an expression of reassurance when the second shock

111

came. This one was no mild shimmy but the real sea-sick roll.

In every Californian, native born or grafted, there is a deep-rooted primitive reflex. An earthquake fills him with soul-shaking claustrophobia which impels him blindly to *get outdoors*! Model boy scouts will push aged grandmothers aside to obey it. It is a matter of record that Teal and Bailey landed on top of Mrs. Bailey. Therefore, she must have jumped through the window first. The order of precedence cannot be attributed to chivalry; it must be assumed that she was in a readier position to spring.

They pulled themselves together, collected their wits a little, and rubbed sand from their eyes. Their first sensations were relief at feeling the solid sand of the desert land under them. Then Bailey noticed something that brought them to their feet and checked Mrs. Bailey from bursting into the speech that she had ready.

'Where's the house?'

It was gone. There was no sign of it at all. They stood in the centre of flat desolation, the landscape they had seen from the window. But, aside from the tortured, twisted trees there was nothing to be seen but the yellow sky and the luminary overhead, whose furnace-like glare was already almost insufferable.

Bailey looked slowly around, then turned to the architect. 'Well, Teal?' His voice was ominous.

Teal shrugged helplessly. 'I wish I knew. I wish I could even be sure that we were on Earth.'

'Well, we can't stand here. It's sure death if we do. Which direction?'

'Any, I guess. Let's keep a bearing on the Sun.'

They had trudged on for an undetermined distance when Mrs. Bailey demanded a rest. They stopped. Teal said in an aside to Bailey, 'Any ideas?'

'No . . . no, none. Say, do you hear anything?'

Teal listened. 'Maybe – unless it's my imagination.'

'Sounds like an automobile. Say, it *is* an automobile!'

They came to the highway in less than another hundred yards. The automobile, when it arrived, proved to be an elderly, puffing light truck, driven by a rancher. He crunched to a stop at their hail. 'We're stranded. Can you help us out?'

'Sure. Pile in.'

'Where are you headed?'

'Los Angeles.'

'Los Angeles? Say, where is this place?'

'Well, you're right in the middle of the Joshua-Tree National Forest.'

The return was as dispiriting as the Retreat from Moscow. Mr. and Mrs. Bailey sat up in front with the driver while Teal bumped along in the body of the truck, and tried to protect his head from the Sun. Bailey subsidized the friendly rancher to detour to the tesseract house, not because they wanted to see it again, but in order to pick up their car.

At last the rancher turned the corner that brought them back to where they had started. But the house was no longer there.

There was not even the ground floor room. It had vanished. The Baileys, interested in spite of themselves, poked around the foundations with Teal.

'Got any answers for this one, Teal?' asked Bailey.

'It must be that on that last shock it simply fell through into another section of space. I can see now that I should have anchored it at the foundations.'

'That's not all you should have done.'

'Well, I don't see that there is anything to get downhearted about. The house was insured, and we've learned an amazing lot. There are possibilities, man, possibilities! Why, right now I've got a great new revolutionary idea for a house—'

Teal ducked in time. He was always a man of action.

'—AND HE BUILT A CROOKED HOUSE—'

Robert Heinlein, in this story, spends a good part of the beginning describing a tesseract. He does an excellent job, but words alone would go for nothing without a diagram. And even with a diagram, they go for very little. A three-dimensional structure would be bad enough for, as Heinlein says, this would merely be a distorted projection of the four-dimensional tesseract. A diagram on paper is a two dimensional distorted projection of the three-dimensional distorted projection of a four-dimensional tesseract (see Figure 1).

113

The house described in the story as being in the shape of an 'opened-up' tesseract would look like Figure 2. The simpler analogue of an 'opened-up' cube is in Figure 3. If you cut out a shape like Figure 3 in thin cardboard and fold along the creases through the third dimension you can form a cube. Theoretically if you build a three-dimensional structure like Figure 2 and fold the eight cubes through the fourth dimension, you can form a tesseract.

The trouble is you can't actually fold the opened-up tesseract through the fourth dimension, either by means of an earthquake or anything else. A real tesseract in four spatial dimension cannot exist in our three-diamensional world.

(At the time this story appeared in February 1941, by the way, Heinlein himself lived at 1776 Lookout Mountain Avenue in Los Angeles, so that he himself is the 'Hermit of Hollywood' and in the first three paragraphs he is making himself the target for his own satire.)

Questions and Suggestions

1. From Figure 1, build the representation of a tesseract in three dimensions, using Tinker Toy materials. Compare it with a representation of a cube drawn in two dimensions. Are the distortions similar? Can you find the eight cubes (six of them distorted) in the tesseract structure?

2. The tesseract can also be called a 'hypercube'. In those terms what would a hypersphere be? You could also have a hypertetrahedron, a hyperellipsoid and so on. Indeed, you could have an entire four-dimensional geometry of 'hyperspace'. What can you find out about this four-dimensional geometry?

3. What do you suppose n-dimensional geometry is?

4. Heinlein says 'Time is a fourth dimension.' In what way is it a fourth dimension? Do purely three-dimensional objects have real existence in our world? What is an 'instantaneous cube'? How could you detect one? What effect would it have on its surroundings? Can something that can neither be detected nor affect its surroundings be said to exist?

5. If time is a fourth dimension, in what way does it differ from the other three? What are the units of measurement of time as compared with the other three? How does travel through time differ from travel through

the other three? If you can rotate an object through three dimensions, converting length into breadth and so on, could you rotate it through time also, making the length extend into the future, for instance?

6. In Einstein's theory of relativity, 'space-time' is an important concept. What is it?

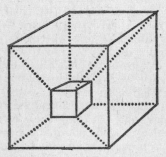

Figure 1

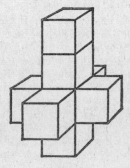

Figure 2

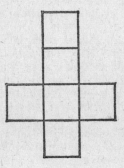

Figure 3

6. PROOF

Hal Clement

Kron held his huge freighter motionless, feeling forward for outside contact. The tremendous interplay of magnectic and electrostatic fields just beyond the city's edge was as clearly perceptible to his senses as the city itself – a mile-wide disc ringed with conical field towers, stretching away behind and to each side. The ship was poised between two of the towers; immediately behind it was the field from which Kron had just taken off. The area was covered with cradles of various forms – cup-shaped receptacles which held city craft like Kron's own: long, boat-shaped hollows wherein reposed the cigarlike vessels which plied between the cities; and towering skeleton frameworks which held upright the slender double cones that hurtled across the dark, lifeless regions between stars.

Beyond the landing field was the city proper; the surface of the disc was covered with geometrically shaped buildings – cones, cylinders, prisms, and hemispheres, jumbled together.

Kron could 'see' all this as easily as a human being in an aeroplane can see New York; but no human eyes could have perceived this city, even if a man could have existed anywhere near it. The city, buildings and all, glowed a savage, white heat; and about and beyond it – a part of it, to human eyes – raged the equally dazzling, incandescent gases of the solar photosphere.

The freighter was preparing to launch itself into that fiery ocean; Kron was watching the play of the artificial reaction fields that supported the city, preparatory to plunging through them at a safe moment.

There was considerable risk of being flattened against the edge of the disc if an inauspicious choice was made, but Kron was an experienced flier, and slipped past the barrier with a sudden, hurtling acceleration that would have pulped any body of flesh and bone. The outer fringe of the field flung the globe sharply downward; then it was free, and the city was dwindling above them.

Kron and four others remained at their posts; the rest

of the crew of thirty relaxed, their spherical bodies lying passive in the cuplike rests distributed through the ship, bathing in the fierce radiance on which those bodies fed, and which was continually streaming from a three-inch spheroid at the centre of the craft. That an artificial source of energy should be needed in such an environment may seem strange, but to these creatures the outer layers of the sun were far more inhospitable to life than is the stratosphere of Earth to human beings.

They had evolved far down near the solar core, where pressures and temperatures were such that matter existed in the 'collapsed' state characteristic of the entire mass of white dwarf stars. Their bodies were simply constructed: a matrix of close-packed electrons – really an unimaginably dense electrostatic field, possessing quasi-solid properties – surrounded a core of neutrons, compacted to the ultimate degree. Radiation of sufficient energy, falling on the 'skin', was stabilized, altered to the pattern and structure of neutrons; the tiny particles of neutronium which resulted were borne along a circulatory system – of magnetic fields, instead of blood – to the nucleus, where it was stored.

The race had evolved to the point where no material appendages were needed. Projected beams and fields of force were their limbs, powered by the annihilation of some of their own neutron substance. Their strange senses gave them awareness not only of electromagnetic radiation, permitting them to 'see' in a more or less normal fashion, but also of energies still undreamed of by human scientists. Kron, hundreds of miles below the city now, was still dimly aware of its location, though radio waves, light and gamma rays were all hopelessly fogged in the clouds of free electrons. At his goal, far down in the solar interior, 'seeing' conditions would be worse – anything more than a few hundred yards distant would be quite indetectable even to him.

Poised beside Kron, near the centre of the spheroidal sun ship, was another being. Its body was ovoid in shape, like that of the Solarian, but longer and narrower, while the ends were tipped with pyramidal structures of neutronium, which projected through the 'skin'. A second, fainter static aura enveloped the creature outside the principal surface; and as the crew relaxed in their cups, a beam of energy from this envelope impinged on Kron's body. It carried a meaning, transmitting a clear thought from one being to the other.

'I still find difficulty in believing my senses,' stated the stranger. 'My own worlds revolve about another which is somewhat similar to this; but such a vast and tenuous atmosphere is most unlike conditions at home. Have you ever been away from Sol?'

'Yes,' replied Kron, 'I was once on the crew of an interstellar projectile. I have never seen your star, however; my acquaintance with it is entirely through hearsay. I am told it consists almost entirely of collapsed matter, like the core of our own; but there is practically no atmosphere. Can this be so? I should think, at the temperature necessary for life, gases would break free of the core and form an envelope.'

'They tend to do so, of course,' returned the other, 'but our surface gravity is immeasurably greater than anything you have here; even your core pull is less, since it is much less dense than our star. Only the fact that our worlds are small, thus causing a rapid diminution of gravity as one leaves them, makes it possible to get a ship away from them at all; atoms, with only their original velocities, remain within a few miles of the surface.

'But you remind me of my purpose on this world – to check certain points of a new theory concerning the possible behaviour of aggregations of normal atoms. That was why I arranged a trip on your flier; I have to make density, pressure, temperature, and a dozen other kinds of measurements at a couple of thousand different levels, in your atmosphere. While I'm doing it, would you mind telling me why you make these regular trips – and why, for that matter, you live so far above your natural level? I should think you would find life easier below, since there would be no need to remain in sealed buildings, or to expend such a terrific amount of power in supporting your cities.'

Kron's answer was slow.

'We make the journeys to obtain neutronium. It is impossible to convert enough power from the immediate neighbourhood of the cities to support them; we must descend periodically for more, even though our converters take so much as to lower the solar temperature considerably for thousands of miles around each city.

118

'The trips are dangerous – you should have been told that. We carry a crew of thirty, when two would be enough to man this ship, for we must fight, as well as fly. You spoke truly when you said that the lower regions of Sol are our natural home; but for æons we have not dared to make more than fleeting visits, to steal the power which is life to us.

'Your little worlds have been almost completely subjugated by your people, Sirian; they never had life forms sufficiently powerful to threaten your domination. But Sol, whose core alone is far larger than the Sirius B pair, did develop such creatures. Some are vast, stupid, slow-moving or immobile; others are semi-intelligent, and rapid movers; all are more than willing to ingest the ready-compacted neutronium of another living being.'

Kron's tale was interrupted for a moment, as the Sirian sent a ray probing out through the ship's wall, testing the physical state of the inferno beyond. A record was made, and the Solarian resumed.

'We, according to logical theory, were once just such a race – of small intelligence, seeking the needs of life among a horde of competing organisms. Our greatest enemy was a being much like ourselves in size and power – just slightly superior in both ways. We were somewhat ahead in intelligence, and I suppose we owe them some thanks – without the competition they provided, we should not have been forced to develop our minds to their present level. We learned to co-operate in fighting them, and from that came the discovery that many of us together could handle natural forces that a single individual could not even approach, and survive. The creation of force effects that had no counterpart in nature was the next step; and, with the understanding of them, our science grew.

'The first cities were of neutronium, like those of to-day, but it was necessary to stabilize the neutrons with fields of energy; at core temperature, as you know, neutronium is a gas. The cities were spherical and much smaller than our present ones. For a long time, we managed to defend them.

'But our enemies evolved, too; not in intelligence, but in power and fecundity. With overspecialization of their physical powers, their mentalities actually degenerated; they became little more than highly organized machines, driven, by an age-old enmity towards our race, to seek us out and destroy us. Their new powers at last enabled them to neutralize, by brute force, the fields which held our cities in shape; and then it was that, from necessity, we fled to the wild, inhospitable upper regions of Sol's atmosphere. Many cities were destroyed by the enemy before a means of supporting them was devised; many more fell victims to forces which we generated, without being able to control, in the effort. The dangers of our present-day trips seem trivial beside those our ancestors braved, in spite of the fact that ships not infrequently fail to return from their flights. Does that answer your question?'

The Sirian's reply was hesitant. 'I guess it does. You of Sol must have developed far more rapidly than we, under that drive; your science, I know, is superior to ours in certain ways, although it was my race which first developed space flight.'

'You had greater opportunities in that line,' returned Kron. 'Two small stars, less than a diameter apart, circling a larger one at a distance incomparably smaller than the usual interstellar interval, provided perfect ground for experimental flights; between your world and mine, even radiation requires some one hundred and thirty rotations to make the journey, and even the nearest other star is almost half as far.

'But enough of this – history is considered by too many to be a dry subject. What brings you on a trip with a power flier? You certainly have not learned anything yet which you could not have been told in the city.'

During the conversation, the Sirian had periodically tested the atmosphere beyond the hull. He spoke, rather absently, as though concentrating on something other than his words.

'I would not be too sure of that, Solarian. My measurements are of greater delicacy than we have ever before achieved. I am looking for a very special effect, to substantiate or disprove an hypothesis which I have recently advanced – much to the detriment of my prestige. If you are interested, I might explain: laugh afterwards if you care to – you will not be the first.

'The theory is simplicity itself. It has occurred to me that matter —— ordinary substances like iron and calcium – might actually take on solid form, like neutronium, under the proper conditions. The normal gas, you know, consists of minute particles travelling with considerable speed in all directions. There seems to be no way of telling whether or not these atoms exert appreciable forces on each other; but it seems to be that if they were brought closely enough together, or slowed down sufficiently, some such effects might be detected.'

'How and why?' asked Kron. 'If the forces are there, why should they not be detectable under ordinary conditions?'

'Tiny changes in velocity due to mutual attraction or repulsion would scarcely be noticed, when the atomic speeds are of the order of hundreds of kilometres per second,' returned the Sirian. 'The effects I seek to detect are of a different nature. Consider, please. We know the sizes of the various atoms, from their radiations. We also know that, under normal conditions, a given mass of any particular gas fills a certain volume. If, however, we surround this gas with an impenetrable container and exert pressure, that volume decreases. We would expect that decrease to be proportional to the pressure, except for an easily determined constant due to the size of the atoms, if no interatomic forces existed; to detect such forces, I am making a complete series of pressure-density tests, more delicate than any heretofore, from the level of your cities down to the neutron core of your world.

'If we could reduce the kinetic energy of the atoms – slow down their motions of translation – the task would probably be simpler; but I see no way to accomplish that. Perhaps, if we could negate nearly all of that energy, the interatomic forces would actually hold the atoms in definite relative positions, approximating the solid state. It was that somewhat injudicious and perhaps too imaginative suggestion which caused my whole idea to be ridiculed on Sirius.'

The ship dropped several hundred miles in the few seconds before Kron answered; since gaseous friction is independent of change in density, the high pressures of the regions being penetrated would be no bar to high speed of flight. Unfortunately, the viscosity of a gas does increase directly as the square root of its temperature; and at the lower levels of the sun, travel would be slow.

'Whether or not our scientists will listen to you, I

cannot say,' said Kron finally. 'Some of them are a rather imaginative crowd, I guess, and none of them will ignore any data you may produce.

'I do not laugh, either. My reason will certainly interest you, as your theory intrigues me. It is the first time anyone has accounted even partly for the things that happened to us on one of my flights.'

The other members of the crew shifted slightly on their cradles; a ripple of interest passed through them, for all had heard rumours and vague tales of Kron's time in the space carrier fleets. The Sirian settled himself more comfortably; Kron dimmed the central globe of radiance a trifle, for the outside temperature was now considerably higher, and began the tale.

'This happened towards the end of my career in space. I had made many voyages with the merchant and passenger vessels, had been promoted from the lowest ranks, through many rotations, to the post of independent captain. I had my own cruiser – a special long-period explorer, owned by the Solarian government. She was shaped like our modern interstellar carriers, consisting of two cones, bases together, with the field ring just forward of their meeting point. She was larger than most, being designed to carry fuel for exceptionally long flights.

'Another cruiser, similar in every aspect, was under the command of a comrade of mine, named Akro; and the two of us were commissioned to transport a party of scientists and explorers to the then newly discovered Fourth System, which lies, as you know, nearly in the plane of the Solar equator, but about half again as distant as Sirius.

'We made good time, averaging nearly half the speed of radiation, and reached the star with a good portion of our hulls still unconsumed. We need not have worried about that, in any case; the star was denser even than the Sirius B twins, and neutronium was very plentiful. I restocked at once, plating my inner walls with the stuff until they had reached their original thickness, although experience indicated that the original supply was ample to carry us either back to Sol, to Sirius, or to Procyon B.

'Akro, at the request of the scientists, did not refuel. Life was present on the star, as it seems to be on all stars where the atomic velocities and the density are high enough; and the biologists wanted to bring back specimens. That meant that room would be needed, and if Akro replated his walls to normal thickness that room would be lacking – as I have mentioned, these were special long-range craft, and a large portion of their volume consisted of available neutronium.

'So it happened that the other ship left the Fourth System with a low, but theoretically sufficient, stock of fuel, and half a dozen compartments filled with specimens of alien life. I kept within detection distance at all times, in case of trouble, for some of those life forms were as dangerous as those of Sol, and, like them, all consumed neutronium. They had to be kept well under control to safeguard the very walls of the ship, and it is surprisingly difficult to make a wild beast, surrounded by food, stay on short rations.

'Some of the creatures proved absolutely unmanageable; they had to be destroyed. Others were calmed by lowering the atomic excitation of their compartments, sending them into a stupor; but the scientists were reluctant to try that in most cases, since not all of the beings could stand such treatment.

'So, for nearly four hundred Solar rotations, Akro practically fought his vessel across space – fought successfully. He managed on his own power until we were within a few hundred diameters of Sol; but I had to help him with the landing – or try to, for the landing was never made.

'It may seem strange, but there is a large volume of space in the neighbourhod of the Sun which is hardly ever traversed. The normal landing orbit arches high over one of the poles of rotation, enters atmosphere almost tangentially somewhere between that pole and the equator, and kills as much as remains of the ship's velocity in the outer atmospheric layers. There is a minimum of magnetic interference that way, since the flier practically coasts along the lines of force of the Solar magnetic field.

'As a result, few ships pass through the space near the plane of the Solar equator. One or two may have done so before us, and I know of several that searched the region later; but none encountered the thing which we found.

'About the time we would normally have started correcting our orbits for a tangential landing, Akro radiated me the information that he could not possibly control his ship any farther with the power still available to him. His walls were already so thin that radiation loss, ordinarily negligible, was becoming a definite menace to his vessel. All his remaining energy would have to be employed in keeping the interior of his ship habitable.

'The only thing I could do was to attach our ships together with an attractor beam, and make a nearly perpendicular drop to Sol. We would have to take our chances with magnetic and electrostatic disturbances in the city-supporting fields which cover so much of the near-equatorial zones, and try to graze the nucleus of the Sun instead of its outer atmosphere, so that Akro could replenish his rapidly failing power.

'Akro's hull was radiating quite perceptibly now; it made an easy target for an attractor. We connected without difficulty, and our slightly different linear velocities caused us to revolve about each other, pivoting on the centre of mass of our two ships. I cut off my driving fields, and we fell spinning towards Sol.

'I was becoming seriously worried about Akro's chances of survival. The now-alarming energy loss through his almost consumed hull threatened to exhaust his supply long before we reached the core; and we were still more than a hundred diameters out. I could not give him any power; we were revolving about each other at a distance of about one tenth of a Solar diameter. To lessen that distance materially would increase our speed of revolution to a point where the attractor could not overcome centrifugal force; and I had neither power nor time to perform the delicate job of exactly neutralizing our rotary momentum without throwing us entirely off course. All we could do was hope.

'We were somewhere between one hundred and one hundred and fifty diameters out when there occurred the most peculiar phenomenon I have ever encountered. The plane of revolution of our two ships passed near Sol, but was nearly perpendicular to the Solar equator; at the time of which I speak, Akro's ship was almost directly between my flier and the Sun. Observations had just shown that we were accelerating Sunward at an unexpectedly high pace, when a call came from Akro.

' "Kron! I am being pulled away from your attractor! There is a large mass somewhere near, for the pull is gravitational, but it emits no radiation that I can detect. Increase your pull, if you can; I cannot possibly free myself alone."

'I did what I could, which was very little. Since we did not know the location of the disturbing dark body, it was impossible to tell just what I should do to avoid bringing my own or Akro's vessel too close. I think now that if I had released him immediately he would have swung clear, for the body was not large, I believe. Unfortunately, I did the opposite, and nearly lost my own ship as well. Two of my crew were throwing as much power as they could convert and handle into the attractor, and trying to hold it on the still easily visible hull of Akro's ship; but the motions of the latter were so peculiar that aiming was a difficult task. They held the ship as long as we could see it; but quite suddenly the radiations by means of which we perceived the vessel faded out, and before we could find a band which would get through, the sudden cessation of our centripetal acceleration told us that the beam had slipped from its target.

'We found that electromagnetic radiations of wave lengths in the octave above H-alpha would penetrate the interference, and Akro's hull was leaking energy enough to radiate in that band. When we found him, however, we could scarcely believe our senses; his velocity was now nearly at right angles to his former course, and his hull radiation had become far weaker. What terrific force had caused this acceleration, and what strange fields was blanketing the radiation, were questions none of us could answer.

'Strain as we might, not one of us could pick up an erg of radiant energy that might emanate from the thing that had trapped Akro. We could only watch, and endeavour to plot his course relative to our own, at first. Our ships were nearing each other rapidly and we were attempting to determine the time and distance of closest approach, when we were startled by the impact of a communicator beam. Akro was alive! The beam was weak, very weak, showing what an infinitesimal amount of power he felt he could spare. His words were not encouraging.

' "Kron! You may as well cut your attractor, if you are still trying to catch me. No power that I dare apply seems to move me perceptibly in any direction from this course. We are all badly shocked, for we hit something that felt almost solid. The walls, even, are strained, and may go at any time."

' "Can you perceive anything around you?" I returned. "You seem to us to be alone in space, though something is absorbing most of your radiated energy. There must be energies in the cosmos of which we have never dreamed, simply because they did not affect our senses. What do your scientists say?"

' "Very little," was the answer. "They have made a few tests, but they say that anything they project is absorbed without reradiating anything useful. We seem to be in a sort of energy vacuum — it takes everything, and returns nothing."

'This was the most alarming item yet. Even in free space, we had been doubtful of Akro's chances of survival; now they seemed reduced to the ultimate zero.

'Meanwhile, our ships were rapidly approaching each other. As nearly as my navigators could tell, both vessels were pursuing almost straight lines in space. The lines were nearly perpendicular but did not lie in a common plane; their minimum distance apart was about one one-thousandth of a Solar diameter. His velocity seemed nearly constant, while I was accelerating Sunward. It seemed that we would reach the near-intersection point almost simultaneously, which meant that my ship was certain to approach the energy vacuum much too closely. I did not dare to try to pull Akro free with an attractor; it was only too obvious that such an attempt could end in disaster for both vessels. If he could not free himself, he was lost.

'We could only watch helplessly as the point of light marking the position of Akro's flier swept closer and closer. At first, as I have said, it seemed perfectly free in space; but as we looked, the region around it began to radiate feebly. There was nothing recognizable about the vibrations, simply a continuous spectrum, cut off by some interference just below the H-alpha wave length and, at the other end, some three octaves higher. As the emission grew stronger, the visible region around the stranded ship grew larger, fading into nothingness at the edges. Brighter and broader the path of radiance grew, as we swept towards it.'

The same radiance was seriously inconveniencing Gordon Aller, who was supposed to be surveying for a geological map of northern Australia. He was camped by the only waterhole in many miles, and had stayed up long after dark preparing his cameras, barometer, soil kit, and other equipment for the morrow's work.

The arrangement of instruments completed, he did not at once retire to his blankets. With his back against a smooth rock and a short, blackened pipe clenched in his teeth, he sat for some time, pondering. The object of his musing does not matter to us; though his eyes were directed heavenward, he was sufficiently accustomed to the southern sky to render it improbable that he was paying much attention to its beauties.

However that may be, his gaze was suddenly attracted to the zenith. He had often seen stars which appeared to move when near the edge of his field of vision – it is a common illusion; but this one continued to shift as he turned his eyes upwards.

Not far from Achernar was a brilliant white point, which brightened as Aller watched it. It was moving slowly northwards, it seemed; but only a moment was needed for the man to realize that the slowness was illusory. The thing was slashing almost vertically downwards at an enormous speed, and must strike Earth not far from his camp.

Aller was not an astronomer, and had no idea of astronomical distances or speeds. He may be forgiven for thinking of the object as travelling perhaps as fast as a modern fighting plane, and first appearing at a height of two or three miles. The natural conclusion from this belief was that the crash would occur within a few hundred feet of the camp. Aller paled; he had seen pictures of the Devil's Pit in Arizona.

Actually, of course, the meteor first presented itself to his gaze at a height of some eighty miles, and was then travelling at a rate of many miles per second relative to Earth. At that speed, the air presented a practically solid obstacle to its flight, and the object was forced to a fairly constant velocity of ten or twelve hundred yards a second while still nearly ten miles from Earth's surface. It was at that point that Aller's eyes caught up with and succeeded in focusing upon the celestial visitor.

The first burst of light had been radiated by the frightfully compressed and heated air in front of the thing; as the original velocity departed, so did the dazzling light. Aller got a clear view of the meteor at a range of less than five miles, for perhaps ten seconds before the impact. It was still incandescent, radiating a bright cherry-red; this must have been due to the loss from within, for so brief a contact even with such highly heated air could not have warmed the Sun ship's neutronium walls a measurable fraction of a degree.

Aller felt the ground tremble as the vessel struck. A geyser of earth, barely visible in the reddish light of the hull, spouted skyward, to fall back seconds later with a long-drawn-out rumble. The man stared at the spot, two miles away, which was still giving off a faint glow. Were 'shooting stars' as regularly shaped as that? He had seen a smooth, slender body, more than a hundred feet in length, apparently composed of two cones of unequal length, joined together at the bases. Around the longer cone, not far from the point of juncture, was a thick bulging ring; no further details were visible at the distance from which he had observed. Aller's vague recollections of meteorites, seen in various museums, brought images of irregular, clinker-like objects before his mind's eye. What, then, could this thing be?

He was not imaginative enough to think for a moment of any possible extraterrestrial source for an aircraft; when it did occur to him that the object was of artificial origin, he thought more of some experimental machine produced by one of the more progressive Earth nations.

At the thought, Aller strapped a first-aid kit to his side and set out towards the crater, in the face of the obvious fact that nothing human could possibly have survived such a crash. He stumbled over the uneven terrain for a quarter of a mile, and then stopped on a small rise of ground to examine more closely the site of the wreck.

The glow should have died by this time, for Aller had taken all of ten minutes to pick his way those few hundred yards; but the dull-red light ahead had changed to a brilliant-orange radiance against which the serrated edges of the pit were clearly silhouetted. No flames were visible; whence came the increasing heat? Aller attempted to get closer, but a wave of frightfully hot air blistered his face and hands, and drove him back. He took up a station near his former camp, and watched.

If the hull of the flier had been anywhere near its normal thickness, the tremendous mass of neutronium would have sunk through the hardness of rocks as though they were liquid. There was, however, scarcely more than a paper thickness of the substance at any part of the walls; and an upthrust of adamantine volcanic rock not far beneath the surface of the desert proved thick enough to absorb the Sun ship's momentum and to support its still enormous weight. Consequently, the ship was covered only by a thin layer of powdered rock which had fallen back into the crater. The disturbances arising from the now extremely rapid loss of energy from Akro's ship were, as a result, decidedly visible from the surface.

The hull, though thin, was still intact; but its temperature was now far above the melting point of the surrounding rocks. The thin layer of pulverized material above the ship melted and flowed away almost instantly, permitting free radiation to the air above; and so enormous is the specific heat of neutronium that no perceptible lowering of hull temperature occurred.

Aller, from his point of observation, saw the brilliant fan of light that sprang from the pit as the flier's hull was exposed – the vessel itself was invisible to him, since he was only slightly above the level of the crater's mouth. He wondered if the impact of the 'meteor' had released some pent-up volcanic energy, and began to doubt, quite justifiably, if he was at a safe distance. His doubts vanished and were replaced by certainty as the edges of the crater began to glow dull-red, then bright-orange, and slowly subsided out of sight. He began packing the most valuable items of his equipment, while a muted, continuous roaring and occasional heavy thuds from the direction of the pit admonished him to hasten.

When he straightened up, with the seventy-pound pack settled on his shoulders, there was simply a lake of lava where the crater had been. The fiery area spread even as he watched; and without further delay he set off on his own back trail. He could see easily, but the light diffused from the inferno behind him; and he made fairly good time, considering his burden and the fact that he had not slept since the preceding night.

The rock beneath Akro's craft was, as we have said, extremely hard. Since there was relatively free escape upward for the constantly liberated energy, the stratum melted very slowly, gradually letting the vessel sink deeper into the earth. What would have happened if Akro's power supply had been greater is problematical; Aller can tell us only that some five hours after the landing, as he was resting for a few moments near the top of a rocky hillock, the phenomenon came to a cataclysmic end.

A quivering of the earth beneath him caused the surveyor to look back towards his erstwhile camp. The lake of lava, which by this time was the better part of a mile in breadth, seemed curiously agitated. Aller, from his rather poor vantage point, could see huge bubbles of pasty lava hump themselves up and burst, releasing brilliant clouds of vapour. Each cloud illuminated Earth and sky before cooling to invisibility, so that the effect was somewhat similar to a series of lightning flashes.

For a short time — certainly no longer than a quarter of a minute — Aller was able to watch as the activity increased. Then a particularly violent shock almost flung him from the hilltop, and at nearly the same instant the entire volume of molten rock fountained skyward. For an instant it seemed to hang there, a white, raging pillar of liquid and gas; then it dissolved, giving way before the savage thrust of the suddenly released energy below. A tongue of radiance, of an intensity indescribable in mere words, stabbed upwards, into and through the lava, volatizing instantly. A dozen square miles of desert glowed white, then an almost invisible violet, and disappeared in superheated gas. Around the edges of this region, great gouts of lava and immense fragments of solid rock were hurled to all points of the compass.

Radiation exerts pressure; at the temperature found in the cores of stars, that pressure must be measured in thousands of tons per square inch. It was this thrust, rather than the by no means negligible gas pressure of the boiling lava, which wrought most of the destruction.

Aller saw little of what occurred. When the lava was hurled upwards, he had flung an arm across his face to protect his eyes from the glare. That act unquestionably saved his eyesight as the real flash followed; as it was, his body was seared and blistered through the clothing. The second, heavier shock knocked his feet from under him, and he half crawled, half rolled down to the comparative shelter of the little hill. Even here, gusts of hot air almost choked him; only the speed with which the phenomenon ended saved his life.

Within minutes, both the tremblors and hot winds had ceased; and he crawled painfully to the hilltop again to gaze wonderingly at the five-mile-wide crater, ringed by a pile of tumbled, still glowing rock fragments.

Far beneath that pit, shards of neutronium, no more able to remain near the surface than the steel pieces of a wrecked ocean vessel can float on water, were sinking through rock and metal to a final resting place at Earth's heart.

'The glow spread as we watched, still giving no clue to the nature of the substance radiating it,' continued Kron. 'Most of it seemed to originate between us and Akro's ship; Akro himself said that but little energy was being lost on the far side. His messages, during that last brief period as we swept by our point of closest approach, were clear – so clear that we could almost see as he did the tenuous light beyond and ever-thinning walls of his ship; the light that represented but a tiny percentage of the energy being sucked from the hull surface.

'We saw, as though with his own senses, the tiny perforation appear near one end of the ship; saw it extend, with the speed of thought, from one end of the hull to the other, permitting the free escape of all the energy in a single instant; and, from our point of vantage, saw the glowing area where the ship had been suddenly brightened, blazing for a moment almost as brightly as a piece of Sun matter.

'In that moment, every one of us saw the identifying frequencies as the heat from Akro's disrupted ship raised the substance which had trapped him to an energy level which permitted atomic radiation. Every one of us recognized the spectra of iron, of calcium, of carbon and silicon and a score of other elements – Sirian, I tell you that that "trapping field" was *matter* – matter

131

in such a state that it could not radiate, and could offer resistance to other bodies in exactly the fashion of a solid. I thought, and have always thought, that some strange field of force held the atoms in their "solid" positions; you have convinced me that I was wrong. The "field" was the sum of the interacting atomic forces which you are trying to detect. The energy level of that material body was so low that those forces were able to act without interference. The condition you could not conceive of reaching artificially actually exists in nature!'

'You go too fast, Kron,' responded the Sirian. 'Your first idea is far more likely to be the true one. The idea of unknown radiant or static force fields is easy to grasp; the one you propose in its place defies common sense. My theories called for some such conditions as you described; granted the one premise of a sufficiently low energy level; but a place in the real universe so devoid of energy as to absorb that of a well-insulated interstellar flier is utterly inconceivable. I have assumed your tale to be true as to details, though you offer neither witnesses nor records to support it; but I seem to have heard that you have somewhat of a reputation as an entertainer, and you seem quick-witted enough to have woven such a tale on the spot, purely from the ideas I suggested. I compliment you on the tale, Kron; it was entrancing; but I seriously advise you not to make anything more out of it. Shall we leave it at that, my friend?'

'As you will,' replied Kron.

PROOF

Naturally we associate life with the planet Earth. If we think of life on other planets, we think of it on other worlds something like the Earth. Even if the chemistry of the other worlds is different from that of our planet, at least the other worlds are solid.

Can we really think of life on the Sun?

About 1800 the most renowned astronomer in the world was Sir William Herschel who had discovered the planet Uranus, who had studied double stars and globular clusters, who had even estimated the size and shape of the Galaxy. His opinions, therefore, were to be taken seriously.

Herschel wondered if the sunspots might not be holes in the flaming atmosphere of the Sun and if, through these holes, the cold solid body beneath might not be glimpsed. He wondered if there might not be inhabitants on that solid underpinning.

We now know that is not so; that the atmosphere of the Sun, far from being hotter than the regions beneath, is actually the very coolest part of the Sun and that the Sun's deeper layers are enormously hot.

If, then, life were conceivable on the Sun, it would have to be a life associated with matter in the form of great heat, which, in actual fact is the common state of matter in the Universe. In our Solar system, for instance, 99.85 per cent of all the matter present is hot and gaseous, with a temperature of 6000°C. and up. This is the Sun. All the rest of the Solar system – the planets, satellites, asteroids, comets and so on – is comparatively cool at the surface but makes up only 0.15 per cent of all the matter.

If this represents the general division in the rest of the Universe, we might well say that cold, solid matter represents so small a portion of the total that it might well be ignored.

To imagine structures so complex that they can support something analogous to what we call life, and even intelligence, under conditions as alien as that of the Sun, and to do so with scientific plausibility, is no easy task. Hal Clement (his real name is Harry Clement Stubbs) is up to it. This was his first published story, appearing when he was barely out of his teens, and he soon became one of the most prominent of the strictly scientific s.f. writers. (He is now science teacher at Milton Academy, with emphasis on astrology.)

Questions and Suggestions

1. Clement speaks of 'neutronium' in the centres of stars, matter made up of neutrons in contact. What are neutrons? Where are they to be found? How and under what conditions would they come together to form neutronium?

2. What is the average width of an atom and the width of a neutron? How would an atom compare with

a neutron in volume? If the matter in the Sun were converted into neutronium, how big would the Sun be in diameter?

3. Clement speaks of two small stars, very close together, circling each other and both circling Sirius itself. Actually, Sirius does have a small companion that was discovered before it was seen. How is it possible for this to happen? What kind of star is this small companion? It is always assumed that the dwarf companion is only a single star; if it were really a closely spaced double star, as Clement suggests, how could we detect the fact?

4. Clement gives distances as such-and-such a multiple of the Sun's diameter. Is that better than giving them as miles or kilometres, or worse? Why?

5. Clement mentions that the cities use up so much energy 'as to lower the Solar temperature considerably for thousands of miles around each city'. This seems to be a reference to sunspots though Clements doesn't say so specifically. Look up the properties of sunspots and decide whether any of them might be consistent with this notion. Is there anything about the behaviour of sunspots in your opinion which is consistent with this far-out suggestion?

6. *Proof* was published in June 1942. When Clement has an Earthman spot the falling star-vessel he says of the Earthman, 'He was not imaginative enough to think for a moment of any possible extraterrestrial source for an aircraft . . .'. Would Clement have said this if he had written the story ten years later? What happened in the next decade that would have completely altered human reactions to a strange sight in the sky? What would *you* think if you saw a strange gleaming shape in the sky that looked like a ship?

7. What is the significance of the title of the story?

7. A SUBWAY NAMED MOBIUS

A. J. Deutsch

In a complex and ingenious pattern, the subway had spread out from a focus at Park Street. A shunt connected the Lechmere line with the Ashmont for trains southbound, and with the Forest Hills line for those northbound. Harvard and Brookline had been linked with a tunnel that passed through Kenmore Under, and during rush hours every other train was switched through the Kenmore Branch back to Egleston. The Kenmore Branch joined the Maverick Tunnel near Fields Corner. It climbed a hundred feet in two blocks to connect Copley Over with Scollay Square; then it dipped down again to join the Cambridge line at Boylston. The Boylston shuttle had finally tied together the seven principal lines on four different levels. It went into service, you remember, on March 3rd. After that, a train could travel from any one station to any other station in the whole system.

There were two hundred and twenty-seven trains running the subways every weekday, and they carried about a million and a half passengers. The Cambridge-Dorchester train that disappeared on March 4th was Number 86. Nobody missed it at first. During the evening rush, the traffic was a little heavier than usual on that line. But a crowd is a crowd. The ad. posters at the Forest Hills yards looked for 86 about 7.30, but neither of them mentioned its absence until three days later. The controller at the Milk Street Cross-Over called the Harvard checker for an extra train after the hockey game that night, and the Harvard checker relayed the call to the yards. The dispatcher there sent out 87, which had been put to bed at ten o'clock, as usual. He didn't notice that 86 was missing.

It was near the peak of the rush the next morning that Jack O'Brien, at the Park Street Control, called Warren Sweeney at the Forest Hills yards and told him to put another train on the Cambridge run. Sweeney was short, so he went to the board and scanned it for a spare train and crew. Then, for the first time, he noticed that Gallagher had not checked out the night before. He put the tag up and left a note. Gallagher was due on at ten. At ten-thirty, Sweeney was down looking at the board again, and he noticed Gallagher's tag still up, and the note where he had left it. He groused to the checker and asked if Gallagher had come in late. The checker said he hadn't seen Gallagher at all that morning. Then Sweeney wanted to know who was running 86? A few minutes later he found that Dorkin's card was still up, although it was Dorkin's day off. It was 11.30 before he finally realized that he had lost a train.

Sweeney spent the next hour and a half on the phone, and he quizzed every dispatcher, controller, and checker on the whole system. When he finished his lunch at 1.30, he covered the whole net again. At 4.40, just before he left for the day, he reported the matter, with some indignation, to Central Traffic. The phones buzzed through the tunnels and shops until nearly midnight before the general manager was finally notified at his home.

It was the engineer on the main switchbank who, late in the morning on the 6th, first associated the missing train with the newspaper stories about the sudden rash of missing persons. He tipped off the *Transcript,* and by the end of the lunch hour three papers had Extras on the streets. That was the way the story got out.

Kelvin Whyte, the general manager, spent a good part of that afternoon with the police. They checked Gallagher's wife, and Dorkin's. The motorman and the conductor had not been home since the morning of the 4th. By mid-afternoon, it was clear to the police that three hundred and fifty Bostonians, more or less, had been lost with the train. The System buzzed, and Whyte nearly expired with simple exasperation. But the train was not found.

Roger Tupelo, the Harvard mathematician, stepped into the picture the evening of the 6th. He reached Whyte by phone, late, at his home, and told him he had some ideas about the missing train. Then he taxied to Whyte's home in Newton and had the first of many talks with Whyte about Number 86.

Whyte was an intelligent man, a good organizer, and not without imagination. 'But I don't know what you're talking about!' he expostulated.

Tupelo was resolved to be patient. 'This is a very hard thing for *anybody* to understand, Mr. Whyte,' he said. 'I can see why you are puzzled. But it's the only explanation. The train has vanished, and the people on it. But the System is closed. Trains are conserved. It's somewhere on the System!'

Whyte's voice grew louder again. 'And I tell you, Dr. Tupelo, that train is *not* on the System! It is *not*! You can't overlook a seven-car train carrying four hundred passengers. The System has been combed. Do you think I'm trying to *hide* the train?'

'Of course not. Now look, let's be reasonable. We know the train was en route to Cambridge at 8.40 a.m. on the 4th. At least twenty of the missing people probably boarded the train a few minutes earlier at Washington, and forty more at Park Street Under. A few got off at both stations. And that's the last. The ones who were going to Kendall, to Central, to Harvard – they never got there. The train did not get to Cambridge.'

'I know that, Dr. Tupelo,' Whyte said savagely. 'In the tunnel under the Charles River, the train turned into a boat. It left the tunnel and sailed for Africa.'

'No, Mr. Whyte. I'm trying to tell you. It hit a node.'

Whyte was livid. 'What is a node?' he exploded. 'The System keeps the tracks clear. Nothing on the tracks but trains, no nodes left lying around—'

'You still don't understand. A node is not an obstruction. It's a singularity. A pole of high order.'

Tupelo's explanations that night did not greatly clarify the situation for Kelvin Whyte. But at two in the morning, the general manager conceded to Tupelo the privilege of examining the master maps of the System. He put in a call first to the police, who could not assist him with his first attempt to master topology, and then, finally, to Central Traffic. Tupelo taxied down there alone, and pored over the maps till morning. He had coffee and a snail, and then went to Whyte's office.

He found the general manager on the telephone. There was a conversation having to do with another, more elaborate inspection of the Dorchester-Cambridge tunnel under the Charles River. When the conversation ended, Whyte slammed the telephone into its cradle and glared at Tupelo. The mathematician spoke first.

'I think probably it's the new shuttle that did this,' he said.

Whyte gripped the edge of his desk and prowled silently through his vocabulary until he had located some civil words. 'Dr. Tupelo,' he said, 'I have been awake all night going over your theory. I don't understand it at all. I don't know what the Boylston shuttle has to do with this.'

'Remember what I was saying last night about the connective properties of networks?' Tupelo asked quietly. 'Remember the Möbius band we made – the surface with one face and one edge? Remember this—?' and he removed a little glass Klein bottle from his pocket and placed it on the desk.

Whyte sat back in his chair and stared wordlessly at the mathematician. Three emotions marched across his face in quick succession – anger, bewilderment, and utter dejection. Tupelo went on.

'Mr. Whyte, the System is a network of amazing topological complexity. It was already complex before the Boylston shuttle was installed, and of a high order of connectivity. But this shuttle makes the network absolutely unique. I don't fully understand it, but the situation seems to be something like this: the shuttle has made the connectivity of the whole System of an order so high that I don't know how to calculate it. I suspect the connectivity has become infinite.'

The general manager listened as though in a daze. He kept his eyes glued to the little Klein bottle.

'The Möbius band,' Tupelo said, 'has unusual properties because it has a singularity. The Klein bottle, with two singularities, manages to be inside of itself. The topologists know surfaces with as many as a thousand singularities, and they have properties that make the Möbius band and the Klein bottle both look simple. But a network with infinite connectivity must have an infinite number of singularities. Can you imagine what the properties of that network could be?'

After a long pause, Tupelo added: 'I can't either. To tell the truth, the structure of the System, with the Boylston shuttle, is completely beyond me. I can only guess.'

Whyte swivelled his eyes up from the desk at a moment when anger was the dominant feeling within him. 'And you call yourself a mathematician, Professor Tupelo!' he said.

Tupelo almost laughed aloud. The incongruousness,

the absolute foolishness of the situation, all but overwhelmed him. He smiled thinly, and said: 'I'm no topologist. Really, Mr. Whyte, I'm a tyro in the field not much better acquainted with it than you are. Mathematics is a big pasture. I happen to be an algebraist.'

His candour softened Whyte a little. 'Well, then,' he ventured, 'if you don't understand it, maybe we should call in a topologist. Are there any in Boston?'

'Yes and no,' Tupelo answered. 'The best in the world is at Tech.'

Whyte reached for the telephone. 'What's his name?' he asked. 'I'll call him.'

'Merritt Turnbull. He can't be reached. I've tried for three days.'

'Is he out of town?' Whyte asked. 'We'll send for him – emergency.'

'I don't know. Professor Turnbull is a bachelor. He lives alone at the Brattle Club. He has not been seen since the morning of the 4th.'

Whyte was uncommonly perceptive. 'Was he on the train?' he asked tensely.

'I don't know,' the mathematician replied. 'What do you think?'

There was a long silence. Whyte looked alternately at Tupelo and at the glass object on the desk. 'I don't understand it,' he said finally. 'We've looked everywhere on the System. There was no way for the train to get out.'

'The train didn't get out. It's still on the System,' Tupelo said.

'Where?'

Tupelo shrugged. 'The train has no real "where". The whole System is without real "whereness". It's double-valued, or worse.'

'How can we find it?'

'I don't think we can,' Tupelo said.

There was another long silence. Whyte broke it with a loud exclamation. He rose suddenly, and sent the Klein bottle flying across the room. You are crazy, Professor!' he shouted. 'Between midnight tonight and 6 a.m. tomorrow, we'll get every train out of the tunnels. I'll send in three hundred men, to comb every inch of the tracks – every inch of the one hundred and eighty-three miles. We'll find the train! Now, please excuse me.' He glared at Tupelo.

Tupelo left the office. He felt tired, completely exhausted. Mechanically, he walked along Washington Street towards the Essex Station. Halfway down the stairs, he stopped abruptly, looked around him slowly. Then he ascended again to the street and hailed a taxi. At home, he helped himself to a double shot. He fell into bed.

At 3.30 that afternoon he met his class in 'Algebra of Fields and Rings'. After a quick supper at the Crimson Spa, he went to his apartment and spent the evening in a second attempt to analyse the connective properties of the System. The attempt was vain, but the mathematician came to a few important conclusions. At eleven o'clock he telephoned Whyte at Central Traffic.

'I think you might want to consult me during tonight's search,' he said. 'May I come down?'

The general manager was none too gracious about Tupelo's offer of help. He indicated that the System would solve this little problem without any help from harebrained professors who thought that whole subway trains could jump off into the fourth dimension. Tupelo submitted to Whyte's unkindness, then went to bed. At about 4 a.m. the telephone awakened him. His caller was a contrite Kelvin Whyte.

'Perhaps I was a bit hasty last night, Professor,' he stammered. 'You may be able to help us after all. Could you come down to the Milk Street Cross-Over?'

Tupelo agreed readily. He felt none of the satisfaction he had anticipated. He called a taxi, and in less than half an hour he was at the prescribed station. At the foot of the stairs, on the upper level, he saw that the tunnel was brightly lit, as during normal operation of the System. But the platforms were deserted except for a tight little knot of seven men near the far end. As he walked towards the group, he noticed that two were policemen. He observed a one-car train on the track beside the platform. The forward door was open, the car brightly lit, and empty. Whyte heard his footsteps and greeted him sheepishly.

'Thanks for coming down, Professor,' he said, extending his hand. 'Gentlemen, Dr. Roger Tupelo, of Harvard. Dr. Tupelo, Mr. Kennedy, our chief engineer; Mr. Wilson, representing the Mayor; Dr. Gannot, of Mercy Hospital.' Whyte did not bother to introduce the motorman and the two policemen.

'How do you do,' said Tupelo. 'Any results, Mr. Whyte?'

The general manager exchanged embarrassed glances with his companions. 'Well . . . yes, Dr. Tupelo,' he finally answered. 'I think we do have some results, of a kind.'

'Has the train been seen?'

'Yes,' said Whyte. 'That is, practically seen. At least, we know it's somewhere in the tunnels.' The six others nodded their agreement.

Tupelo was not surprised to learn that the train was still on the System. After all, the System was closed. 'Would you mind telling me just what happened?' Tupelo insisted.

'I hit a red signal,' the motorman volunteered. 'Just outside the Copley junction.'

'The tracks have been completely cleared of all trains,' Whyte explained, 'except for this one. We've been riding it, all over the System, for four hours now. When Edmunds, here, hit a red light at the Copley junction, he stopped, of course. I thought the light must be defective, and told him to go ahead. But then we heard another train pass the junction.'

'Did you see it?' Tupelo asked.

'We couldn't see it. The light is placed just behind a curve. But we all heard it. There's no doubt the train went through the junction. And it must be Number 86, because our car was the only other one on the tracks.'

'What happened then?'

'Well, then the light changed to yellow, and Edmunds went ahead.'

'Did he follow the other train?'

'No. We couldn't be sure which way it was going. We must have guessed wrong.'

'How long ago did this happen?'

'At 1.38, the first time—'

'Oh, said Tupelo, 'then it happened again later?'

'Yes, But not at the same spot, of course. We hit another red signal near South Station at 2.15. And then at 3.28—'

Tupelo interrupted the general manager. 'Did you see the train at 2.15?'

'We didn't even hear it, that time. Edmunds tried to catch it, but it must have turned off on to the Boylston shuttle.'

'What happened at 3.28?'

'Another red light. Near Park Street. We heard it up ahead of us.'

'But you didn't see it?'

'No. There is a little slope beyond the light. But we all heard it. The only thing I don't understand, Dr. Tupelo, is how the train could run the tracks for nearly five days without anybody seeing—'

Whyte's words trailed off into silence, and his right hand went up in a peremptory gesture for quiet. In the distance, the low metallic thunder of a fast-rolling train swelled up suddenly into a sharp, shrill roar of wheels below. The platform vibrated perceptibly as the train passed.

'Now we've got it!' Whyte exclaimed. 'Right past the men on the platform below!' He broke into a run towards the stairs to the lower level. All the others followed him, except Tupelo. He thought he knew what was going to happen. Before Whyte reached the stairs, a policeman bounded up to the top.

'Did you see it, now?' he shouted.

Whyte stopped in his tracks, and the others with him.

'Did you see that train?' the policeman from the lower level asked again, as two more men came running up the stairs.

'What happened?' Wilson wanted to know.

'Didn't *you* see it?' snapped Kennedy.

'Sure not,' the policeman replied. 'It passed through up here.'

'It did *not*,' roared Whyte. 'Down there!'

The six men with Whyte glowered at the three men from the lower level. Tupelo walked to Whyte's elbow. 'The train can't be seen, Mr. Whyte,' he said quietly.

Whyte looked down at him in utter disbelief. 'You heard it yourself. It passed right below—'

'Can we go to the car, Mr. Whyte?' Tupelo asked. 'I think we ought to talk a little.'

Whyte nodded dumbly, then turned to the policeman and the others who had been watching at the lower level. 'You really didn't see it?' he begged them.

'We heard it,' the policeman answered. 'It passed up here, going that way, I think,' and he gestured with his thumb.

'Get back downstairs, Maloney,' one of the policemen

with Whyte commanded. Maloney scratched his head, turned, and disappeared below. The two other men followed him. Tupelo led the original group to the car beside the station platform. They went in and took seats, silently. Then they all watched the mathematician and waited.

'You didn't call me down here tonight just to tell me you'd found the missing train.' Tupelo began, looking at Whyte. 'Has this sort of thing happened before?'

Whyte squirmed in his seat and exchanged glances with the chief engineer. 'Not exactly like this,' he said, evasively, 'but there have been some funny things.'

'Like what?' Tupelo snapped.

'Well, like the red lights. The watchers near Kendall found a red light at the same time we hit the one near South Station.'

'Go on.'

'Mr. Sweeney called me from Forest Hills at Park Street Under. He heard the train just two minutes after we heard it at the Copley junction. Twenty-eight track miles away.'

'As a matter of fact, Dr. Tupelo,' Wilson broke in, 'several dozen men have seen lights go red, or have heard the train, or both, inside of the last four hours. The thing acts as though it can be in several places at once.'

'It can,' Tupelo said.

'We keep getting reports of watchers seeing the thing,' the engineer added. 'Well, not exactly seeing it, either, but everything except that. Sometimes at two or even three places, far apart, at the same time. It's sure to be on the tracks. Maybe the cars are uncoupled.'

'Are you really sure it's on the tracks, Mr. Kennedy?' Tupelo asked.

'Positive,' the engineer said. 'The dynamometers at the power house show that it's drawing power. It's been drawing power all night. So at 3.30 we broke the circuits. Cut the power.'

'What happened?'

'Nothing.' Whyte answered. 'Nothing at all. The power was off for twenty minutes. During that time, not one of the two hundred and fifty men in the tunnels saw a red light or heard a train. But the power wasn't on for five minutes before we had two reports again — one from Arlington, the other from Egleston.'

There was a long silence after Whyte finished speaking. In the tunnel below, one man could be heard calling something to another. Tupelo looked at his watch. The time was 5.20.

'In short, Dr. Tupelo,' the general manager finally said, 'we are compelled to admit that there may be something in your theory.' The others nodded agreement.

'Thank you, gentlemen,' Tupelo said.

The physician cleared his throat. 'Now about the passengers,' he began. 'Have you any idea what—?'

'None,' Tupelo interrupted.

'What should we do, Dr. Tupelo?' the mayor's representative asked.

'I don't know. What can you do?'

'As I understand it from Mr. Whyte,' Wilson continued, 'the train has . . . well, it has jumped into another dimension. It isn't really on the System at all. It's just gone. Is that right?'

'In a manner of speaking.'

'And this . . . er . . . peculiar behaviour has resulted from certain mathematical properties associated with the new Boylston shuttle?'

'Correct.'

'And there is nothing we can do to bring the train back to . . . uh . . . this dimension?'

'I know of nothing.'

Wilson took the bit in his teeth. 'In this case, gentlemen,' he said, 'our course is clear. First, we must close off the new shuttle, so this fantastic thing can never happen again. Then, since the missing train is really gone, in spite of all these red lights and noises, we can resume normal operation of the System. At least there will be no danger of collision – which has worried you so much, Whyte. As for the missing train and the people on it—' He gestured them into infinity. 'Do you agree, Dr. Tupelo?' he asked the mathematician.

Tupelo shook his head slowly. 'Not entirely, Mr. Wilson,' he responded. 'Now, please keep in mind that I don't fully comprehend what has happened. It's unfortunate that you won't find anybody who can give a good explanation. The one man who might have done so is Professor Turnbull, of Tech, and he was on the train. But in any case, you will want to check my con-

144

clusions against those of some competent topologists. I can put you in touch with several.

'Now, with regard to the recovery of the missing train, I can say that I think this is not hopeless. There is a finite probability, as I see it, that the train will eventually pass from the nonspatial part of the network, which it now occupies, back to the spatial part. Since the nonspatial part is wholly inaccessible, there is unfortunately nothing we can do to bring about this transition, or even to predict when or how it will occur. But the possibility of the transition will vanish if the Boylston shuttle is taken out. It is just this section of the track that gives the network its essential singularities. If the singularities are removed, the train can never reappear. Is this clear?'

It was not clear, of course, but the seven listening men nodded agreement. Tupelo continued.

'As for the continued operation of the System while the missing train is in the nonspatial part of the network, I can only give you the facts as I see them and leave to your judgment the difficult decision to be drawn from them. The transition back to the spatial part is unpredictable, as I have already told you. There is no way to know when it will occur, or where. In particular, there is a fifty per cent probability that, if and when the train reappears, it will be running on the wrong track. Then there will be a collision, of course.'

The engineer asked: 'To rule out this possibility, Dr. Tupelo, couldn't we leave the Boylston shuttle open, but send no trains through it? Then, when the missing train reappears on the shuttle, it cannot meet another train.'

'That precaution would be ineffective, Mr. Kennedy,' Tupelo answered. 'You see, the train can reappear anywhere on the System. It is true that the System owes its topological complexity to the new shuttle. But, with the shuttle in the System, it is now the whole System that possesses infinite connectivity. In other words, the relevant topological property is a property *derived* from the shuttle, but *belonging* to the whole System. Remember that the train made its first transition at a point between Park and Kendall, more than three miles away from the shuttle.

'There is one question more you will want answered. If you decide to go on operating the System, with the

Boylston shuttle left in until the train reappears, can this happen again, to another train? I am not certain of the answer, but I think it is: No. I believe an exclusion principle operates here, such that only one train at a time can occupy the nonspatial network.'

The physician rose from his seat. 'Dr. Tupelo,' he began, timorously, 'when the train does reappear, will the passengers—?'

'I don't know about the people on the train,' Tupelo cut in. 'The topological theory does not consider such matters.' He looked quickly at each of the seven tired, querulous faces before him. 'I am sorry, gentlemen,' he added, somewhat more gently. 'I simply do not know.' To Whyte, he added: 'I think I can be of no more help tonight. You know where to reach me.' And, turning on his heel, he left the car and climbed the stairs. He found dawn spilling over the street, dissolving the shadows of night.

That impromptu conference in a lonely subway car was never reported in the papers. Nor were the full results of the night-long vigil over the dark and twisted tunnels. During the week that followed, Tupelo participated in four more formal conferences with Kelvin Whyte and certain city officials. At two of these, other topologists were present. Ornstein was imported to Boston from Philadelphia, Kashta from Chicago, and Michaelis from Los Angeles. The mathematicians were unable to reach a consensus. None of the three would fully endorse Tupelo's conclusions, although Kashta indicated that there *might* be something to them. Ornstein averred that a finite network could not possess infinite connectivity, although he could not prove this proposition and could not actually calculate the connectivity of the System. Michaelis expressed his opinion that the affair was a hoax and had nothing whatever to do with the topology of the System. He insisted that if the train could not be found on the System then the System must be open, or at least must once have been open.

But the more deeply Tupelo analysed the problems, the more fully he was convinced of the essential correctness of his first analysis. From the point of view of topology, the System soon suggested whole families of multiple-valued networks, each with an infinite number of

146

infinite discontinuities. But a definite discussion of these new spatio-hyperspatial networks somehow eluded him. He gave the subject his full attention for only a week. Then his other duties compelled him to lay the analysis aside. He resolved to go back to the problem later in the Spring, after courses were over.

Meanwhile, the System was operated as though nothing untoward had happened. The general manager and the mayor's representative had somehow managed to forget the night of the search, or at least to reinterpret what they had seen and not seen. The newspapers and the public at large speculated wildly, and they kept continuing pressure on Whyte. A number of suits were filed against the System on behalf of persons who had lost a relative. The State stepped into the affair and prepared its own thorough investigation. Recriminations were sounded in the halls of Congress. A garbled version of Tupelo's theory eventually found its way into the press. He ignored it, and it was soon forgotten.

The weeks passed, and then a month. The State's investigation was completed. The newspaper stories moved from the first page to the second; to the twenty-third; and then stopped. The missing persons did not return. In the large, they were no longer missed.

One day in mid-April, Tupelo travelled by subway again, from Charles Street to Harvard. He sat stiffly in front of the first car, and watched the tracks and grey tunnel walls hurl themselves at the train. Twice the train stopped for a red light, and Tupelo found himself wondering whether the other train was really just ahead, or just beyond space. He half-hoped, out of curiosity, that his exclusion principle was wrong, that the train might make the transition. But he arrived at Harvard on time. Only he among the passengers had found the trip exciting.

The next week he made another trip by subway, and again the next. As experiments, they were unsuccessful, and much less tense than the first ride in mid-April. Tupelo began to doubt his own analysis. Sometime in May, he reverted to the practice of commuting by subway between his Beacon Hill apartment and his office at Harvard. His mind stopped racing down the knotted grey caverns ahead of the train. He read the morning

147

newspaper, or the abstracts in *Reviews of Modern Mathematics*.

Then there was one morning when he looked up from the newspaper and sensed something. He pushed panic back on its stiff, quivering spring, and looked quickly out of the window at his right. The lights of the car showed the black and grey lines of wall-spots streaking by. The tracks ground out their familiar steely dissonance. The train rounded a curve and crossed a junction that he remembered. Swiftly, he recalled boarding the train at Charles, noting the girl on the ice-carnival poster at Kendall, meeting the southbound train going into Central.

He looked at the man sitting beside him, with a lunch pail on his lap. The other seats were filled, and there were a dozen or so straphangers. A mealy-faced youth near the front door smoked a cigarette, in violation of the rules. Two girls behind him across the aisle were discussing a club meeting. In the seat ahead, a young woman was scolding her little son. The man on the aisle, in the seat ahead of that, was reading the paper. The Transit-Ad above him extolled Florida oranges.

He looked again at the man two seats ahead and fought down the terror within. He studied that man. What was it? Brunet, greying hair; a roundish head; wan complexion; rather flat features; a thick neck, with the hairline a little low, a little ragged; a grey, pinstripe suit. While Tupelo watched, the man waved a fly away from his left ear. He swayed a little with the train. His newpaper was folded vertically down the middle. His *newspaper*! It was last March's!

Tupelo's eyes swivelled to the man beside him. Below his lunch pail was a paper. Today's. He turned in his seat and looked behind him. A young man held the *Transcript* open to the sports pages. The date was March 4th. Tupelo's eyes raced up and down the aisle. There were a dozen passengers carrying papers ten weeks old.

Tupelo lunged out of his seat. The man on the aisle muttered a curse as the mathematician crowded in front of him. He crossed the aisle in a bound and pulled the cord above the windows. The brakes sawed and screeched at the tracks, and the train ground to a stop. The startled passengers eyed Tupelo with hostility. At the rear of the car, the door flew open and a tall, thin man in a blue uniform burst in. Tupelo spoke first.

'Mr. Dorkin?' he called, vehemently.

The conductor stopped short and groped for words.

'There's been a serious accident, Dorkin,' Tupelo said, loudly, to carry over the rising swell of protest from the passengers. 'Get Gallagher back here right away!'

Dorkin reached up and pulled the cord four times. 'What happened?' he asked.

Tupelo ignored the question, and asked one of his own.

'Where have you been, Dorkin?'

The conductor's face was blank. 'In the next car, but—'

Tupelo cut him off. He glanced at his watch, then shouted at the passengers. 'It's ten minutes to nine on May 17th!'

The announcement stilled the rising clamour for a moment. The passengers exchanged bewildered glances.

'Look at your newspapers!' Tupelo shouted. 'Your newspapers!'

The passengers began to buzz. As they discovered each other's papers, the voices rose. Tupelo took Dorkin's arm and led him to the rear of the car. 'What time is it?' he asked.

'8.21,' Dorkin said, looking at his watch.

'Open the door,' said Tupelo, motioning ahead. 'Let me out. Where's the phone?'

Dorkin followed Tupelo's directions. He pointed to a niche in the tunnel wall a hundred yards ahead. Tupelo vaulted to the ground and raced down the narrow lane between the cars and the wall. 'Central Traffic!' he barked at the operator. He waited a few seconds, and saw a train had stopped at the red signal behind his train. Flashlights were advancing down the tunnel. He saw Gallagher's legs running down the tunnel on the other side of 86. 'Get me Whyte!' he commanded, when Central Traffic answered. 'Emergency!'

There was a delay. He heard voices rising from the train beside him. The sound was mixed – anger, fear, hysteria.

'Hello!' he shouted. 'Hello! Emergency! Get me Whyte!'

'I'll take it,' a man's voice said at the other end of the line. 'Whyte's busy!'

'Number 86 is back,' Tupelo called. 'Between Central

and Harvard now. Don't know when it made the jump. I caught it at Charles ten minutes ago, and didn't notice it till a minute ago.'

The man at the other end gulped hard enough to carry over the telephone. 'The passengers?' he croaked.

'All right, the ones that are left,' Tupelo said. 'Some must have got off already at Kendall and Central.'

'Where have they been?'

Tupelo dropped the receiver from his ear and stared at it, his mouth wide open. Then he slammed the receiver on to the hook and ran back to the open door.

Eventually, order was restored, and within a half hour the train proceeded to Harvard. At the station, the police took all passengers into protective custody. Whyte himself arrived at Harvard before the train did. Tupelo found him on the platform.

Whyte motioned weakly towards the passengers. 'They're really all right?' he asked.

'Perfectly,' said Tupelo. 'Don't know they've been gone.'

'Any sign of Professor Turnbull?' asked the general manager.

'I didn't see him. He probably got off at Kendall, as usual.'

'Too bad,' said Whyte. 'I'd like to see him!'

'So would I!' Tupelo answered. 'By the way, now is the time to close the Boylston shuttle.'

'Now is too late,' Whyte said. 'Train 143 vanished twenty-five minutes ago, between Egleston and Dorchester.'

Tupelo stared past Whyte, and down and down the tracks.

'We've got to find Turnbull,' Whyte said.

Tupelo looked at Whyte and smiled thinly.

'Do you really think Turnbull got off this train at Kendall?' he asked.

'Of course!' answered Whyte. 'Where else?'

A SUBWAY NAMED MOBIUS

The germ of the plot of this story rests in the 'Möbius strip' so-called because its properties were first carefully analysed by a German mathematician, August Ferdinand Möbius, in the mid-nineteenth century.

150

You can easily construct a Möbius strip for yourself. Take a piece of ordinary note paper about eleven inches long and cut a strip half an inch wide. Bend it in a circle so that the two short edges overlap. Give one of the ends a single twist and then paste them together so that the bottom side of one end adjoins the top side of the other, as overleaf.

The Möbius strip possesses only one side. If you make a pencil mark along the strip anywhere and keep drawing that mark till you return to the starting point, you will find the mark on the side that seems below as well as on that which seems above. The single side is both below and above. For the same reason, the Möbius strip possesses only one edge.

The most startling property of the Möbius strip is revealed when the strip is sliced longwise down its centre. From experience with similar objects of the ordinary type, with two sides and two edges (such as a ring of paper formed by pasting a strip together *without* a twist), you would expect to form two strips just like the original but each one only half as wide. This does not happen with the Möbius strip. Try it and see.

The properties of the Möbius strip are an example of the sort of thing studied in that branch of mathematics called 'topology'. The study of topology leads to the discovery and analysis of all kinds of figures very different from the common ones of everyday life. Their properties are so unusual that it is easy to imagine that you could build a subway network so complicated that its properties would be paradoxical in the fashion of the Möbius strip, only more so.

(The title of the story, by the way, borrows from the famous Tennessee Williams play, *A Streetcar Named Desire*, which was produced three years before this story was published.)

Questions and Suggestions

1. Read an introductory book on topology and note some of the unusual properties of odd figures. In particular, what are the properties of the 'Klein bottle' which is briefly mentioned in the story? How did it get its name?

2. In 1950, when Deutsch (who died in 1969) wrote the story, he was in the astronomy department at Harvard. Naturally, then, he wrote the story about the Bos-

ton subway system. Get a map of the Boston subway system (which is by no means as complicated as that of New York) and follow the references in the story. Did Deutsch exaggerate the complexity of the system? Could the system, however complex, develop the kind of topological oddness Deutsch describes?

3. There is an odd coincidence in the story that has nothing to do with the story itself and that Deutsch could not have planned. One of the chief characters in the story is Kelvin Whyte. Well, in 1967, Boston elected a man named Kevin White as mayor and he is still in that office as I write this. Another example (and an even stranger one) involves a story called *Merman* written by L. Sprague de Camp in 1940. In that story, de Camp's hero was an ichthyologist named Vernon Brock. Unknown to de Camp there was a real ichthyologist named Vernon Brock, who read science fiction and promptly wrote to de Camp. Fortunately, he was not annoyed. Such coincidences abound everywhere. What do you think of them? Suppose I said, 'No matter how weird such coincidences may seem, it would be far more weird to have no such coincidences.' Would you agree? There is a branch of mathematics called probability that deals with such things among others, if you are interested.

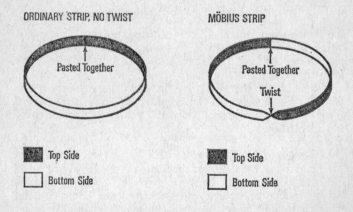

ORDINARY STRIP, NO TWIST

Pasted Together

MÖBIUS STRIP

Pasted Together

Twist

Top Side

Bottom Side

Top Side

Bottom Side

8. SURFACE TENSION

James Blish

Dr. Chatvieux took a long time over the microscope, leaving la Ventura with nothing to do but look out at the dead landscape of Hydrot. Waterscape, he thought, would be a better word. The new world had shown only one small, triangular continent, set amid endless ocean and even the continent was mostly swamp.

The wreck of the seed-ship lay broken squarely across the one real spur of rock Hydrot seemed to possess, which reared a magnificent twenty-one feet above sea-level. From this eminence, la Ventura could see forty miles to the horizon across a flat bed of mud. The red light of the star Tau Ceti, glinting upon thousands of small lakes, pools, ponds, and puddles, made the watery plain look like a mosaic of onyx and ruby.

'If I were a religious man,' the pilot said suddenly, I'd call this a plain case of divine vengeance.'

Chatvieux said: 'Hmm?'

'It's as if we've been struck down for – is it *hubris,* arrogant pride?'

'Well, is it?' Chatvieux said, looking up at last. 'I don't feel exactly swollen with pride at the moment. Do you?'

'I'm not exactly proud of my piloting,' la Ventura admitted. 'But that isn't quite what I meant. I was thinking about why we came here in the first place. It takes arrogant pride to think that you can scatter men, or at least things like men, all over the face of the Galaxy. It takes even more pride to do the job – to pack up all the equipment and move from planet to planet and actually make men suitable for every place you touch.'

'I suppose it does,' Chatvieux said. 'But we're only one of several hundred seed-ships in this limb of the Galaxy, so I doubt that the gods picked us out as special sinners.' He smiled drily. 'If they had, maybe they'd have left us our ultraphone, so the Colonization Council could hear about our cropper. Besides, Paul, we try to produce men adapted to Earthlike planets, nothing more. We've sense enough – humility enough, if you like – to know that we can't adapt men to Jupiter or to Tau Ceti.'

'Anyhow, we're here,' la Ventura said grimly. 'And we aren't going to get off. Phil tells me that we don't even have our germ-cell bank any more, so we can't seed this place in the usual way. We've been thrown on to a dead world and dared to adapt it. What are the panatropes going to do – provide built-in waterwings?'

'No,' Chatvieux said calmly. 'You and I and the rest of us are going to die, Paul. Panatropic techniques don't work on the body, only on the inheritance-carrying factors. We can't give you built-in waterwings, any more than we can give you a new set of brains. I think we'll be able to populate this world with men, but we won't live to see it.'

The pilot thought about it, a lump of cold collecting gradually in his stomach. 'How long do you give us?' he said at last.

'Who knows? A month, perhaps.'

The bulkhead leading to the wrecked section of the ship was pushed back, admitting salty, muggy air, heavy with carbon dioxide. Philip Strasvogel, the communications officer, came in, tracking mud. Like la Ventura, he was now a man without a function, but it did not appear to bother him. He unbuckled from around his waist a canvas belt into which plastic vials were stuffed like cartridges.

'More samples, Doc,' he said. 'All alike – water, very wet. I have some quicksand in one boot, too. Find anything?'

'A good deal, Phil. Thanks. Are the others around?'

Strasvogel poked his head out and hallooed. Other voices rang out over the mudflats. Minutes later, the rest of the survivors were crowding into the panatrope deck: Saltonstall, Chatvieux's senior assistant; Eunice Wagner, the only remaining ecologist; Eleftherios Venezuelos, the delegate from the Colonization Council; and Joan Heath, a midshipman whose duties, like la Ventura's and Strasvogel's, were now without meaning.

Five men and two women – to colonize a planet on which standing room meant treading water.

They came in quietly and found seats or resting places on the deck, on the edges of tables, in corners.

Venezuelos said: 'What's the verdict, Dr. Chatvieux?'

'This place isn't dead,' Chatvieux said. 'There's life in

the sea and in the fresh water, both. On the animal side of the ledger, evolution seems to have stopped with the crustacea; the most advanced form I've found is a tiny crayfish, from one of the local rivulets. The ponds and puddles are well-stocked with protozoa and small metazoans, right up to wonderfully variegated rotifer population – including a castle-building rotifer like Earth's *Floscularidae*. The plants run from simple algae to the thalluslike species.'

'The sea is about the same,' Eunice said, 'I've found some of the larger simple metazoans – jellyfish and so on – and some crayfish almost as big as lobsters. But it's normal to find saltwater species running larger than fresh-water.'

'In short,' Chatvieux said, 'we'll survive here – if we fight.'

'Wait a minute,' la Ventura said. 'You've just finished telling me that we wouldn't survive. And you were talking about us, not about the species, because we don't have our germ-cell banks any more. What's—'

'I'll get to that again in a moment,' Chatvieux said. 'Saltonstall, what would you think of taking to the sea? We came out of it once; maybe we could come out of it again.'

'No good,' Saltonstall said immediately. '*I* like the idea, but I don't think this planet ever heard of Swinburne, or Homer, either. Looking at it as a colonization problem, as if we weren't involved ourselves, I wouldn't give you a credit for *epi oinopa ponton*. The evolutionary pressure there is too high, the competition from other species is prohibitive; seeding the sea should be the last thing we attempt. The colonists wouldn't have a chance to learn a thing before they were destroyed.'

'Why?' la Ventura said. The death in his stomach was becoming hard to placate.

'Eunice, do your sea-going Coelenterates include anything like the Portuguese man-of-war?'

The ecologist nodded.

'There's your answer, Paul,' Saltonstall said. 'The sea is out. It's got to be fresh water, where the competing creatures are less formidable and there are more places to hide.'

'We can't compete with a jellyfish?' la Ventura asked, swallowing.

'No, Paul,' Chatvieux said. 'The panatropes make

adaptations, not gods. They take human germ-cells – in this case, our own, since our bank was wiped out in the crash – and modify them towards creatures who can live in any reasonable environment. The result will be manlike and intelligent. It usually shows the donor's personality pattern, too.

'*But we can't transmit memory*. The adapted man is worse than a child in his new environment. He has no history, no techniques, no precedents, not even a language. Ordinarily the seeding teams more or less take him through elementary school before they leave the planet, but we won't survive long enough for that. We'll have to design our colonists with plenty of built-in protections and locate them in the most favourable environment possible, so that at least some of them will survive the learning process.'

The pilot thought about it, but nothing occurred to him which did not make the disaster seem realer and more intimate with each passing second. 'One of the new creatures can have my personality pattern, but it won't be able to remember being me. Is that right?'

'That's it. There may be just the faintest of residuums – panatropy's given us some data which seem to support the old Jungian notion of ancestral memory. But we're all going to die on Hydrot, Paul. There's no avoiding that. Somewhere we'll leave behind people who behave as we would, think and feel as we would, but who won't remember la Ventura, or Chatvieux, or Joan Heath – or Earth.'

The pilot said nothing more. There was a grey taste in his mouth.

'Saltonstall, what do you recommend as a form?'

The panatropist pulled reflectively at his nose. 'Webbed extremities, of course, with thumbs and big toes heavy and thornlike for defence until the creature has had a chance to learn. Book-lungs, like the arachnids, working out of intercostal spiracles – they are gradually adaptable to atmosphere-breathing if it ever decides to come out of the water. Also I'd suggest sporulation. As an aquatic animal, our colonist is going to have an indefinite life-span, but we'll have to give it a breeding cycle of about six weeks to keep its numbers up during the learning period; so there'll have to be a definite break of some duration in its active year. Otherwise it'll hit the population problem before it's learned enough to cope with it.'

'Also, it'll be better if our colonists could winter inside a good hard shell,' Eunice Wagner added in agreement. 'So sporulation's the obvious answer. Most microscopic creatures have it.'

'Microscopic?' Phil said incredulously.

'Certainly,' Chatvieux said, amused. 'We can't very well crowd a six-foot man into a two-foot puddle. But that raises a question. We'll have tough competition from the rotifers, and some of them aren't strictly microscopic. I don't think your average colonist should run under 25 microns, Saltonstall. Give them a chance to slug it out.'

'I was thinking of making them twice that big.'

'Then they'd be the biggest things in their environment,' Eunice Wagner pointed out, 'and won't ever develop any skills. Besides, if you make them about rotifer size, it'll give them an incentive for pushing out the castle-building rotifers.

'They'll be able to take over the castles as dwellings.'

Chatvieux nodded. 'All right, let's get started. While the panatropes are being calibrated, the rest of us can put our heads together on leaving a record for these people. We'll microengrave the record on a set of corrosion-proof metal leaves, of a size our colonists can handle conveniently. Some day they may puzzle it out.'

'Question,' Eunice Wagner said. 'Are we going to tell them they're microscopic? I'm opposed to it. It'll saddle their entire early history with a gods-and-demons mythology they'd be better off without.'

'Yes, we are,' Chatvieux said; and la Ventura could tell by the change in the tone of his voice that he was speaking now as their senior. 'These people will be of the race of men, Eunice. We want them to win their way back to the community of men. They are not toys, to be protected from the truth forever in a fresh-water womb.'

'I'll make that official,' Venezuelos said, and that was that.

And then, essentially, it was all over. They went through the motions. Already they were beginning to be hungry. After la Ventura had had his personality pattern recorded, he was out of it. He sat by himself at the far end of the ledge, watching Tau Ceti go redly

157

down, chucking pebbles into the nearest pond, wondering morosely which nameless puddle was to be his Lethe.

He never found out, of course. None of them did.

I

Old Shar set down the heavy metal plate at last, and gazed instead out of the window of the castle, apparently resting his eyes on the glowing green-gold obscurity of the summer waters. In the soft fluorescence which played down upon him, from the Noc dozing impassively in the groined vault of the chamber, Lavon could see that he was in fact a young man. His face was so delicately formed as to suggest that it had not been many seasons since he had first emerged from his spore.

But of course there had been no real reason to expect an old man. All the Shars had been referred to traditionally as 'old' Shar. The reason, like the reasons for everything else, had been forgotten, but the custom had persisted; the adjective at least gave weight and dignity to the office.

The present Shar belonged to the generation XVI, and hence would have to be at least two seasons younger than Lavon himself. If he was old, it was only in knowledge.

'Lavon, I'm going to have to be honest with you,' Shar said at last, still looking out of the tall, irregular window. 'You've come to me for the secrets on the metal plates, just as your predecessors did to mine. I can give some of them to you – but for the most part, I don't know what they mean.'

'After so many generations?' Lavon asked, surprised. 'Wasn't it Shar III who first found out how to read them? That was a long time ago.'

The young man turned and looked at Lavon with eyes made dark and wide by the depths into which they had been staring. 'I can read what's on the plates, but most of it seems to make no sense. Worst of all, the plates are incomplete. You didn't know that? They are. One of them was lost in a battle during the final war with the Eaters, while these castles were still in their hands.'

'What am I here for, then?' Lavon said. 'Isn't there anything of value on the remaining plates? Do they

158

really contain "the wisdom of the Creators" or is that another myth?'

'No. No, that's true,' Shar said slowly, 'as far as it goes.'

He paused, and both men turned and gazed at the ghostly creature which had appeared suddenly outside the window. Then Shar said gravely, 'Come in, Para.'

The slipper-shaped organism, nearly transparent except for the thousands of black-and-silver granules and frothy bubbles which packed its interior, glided into the chamber and hovered, with a muted whirring of cilia. For a moment it remained silent, probably speaking telepathically to the Noc floating in the vault, after the ceremonious fashion of all the protos. No human had ever intercepted one of these colloquies, but there was no doubt about their reality: humans had used them for long-range communication for generations.

Then the Para's cilia buzzed once more. Each separate hair-like process vibrated at an independent, changing rate; the resulting sound waves spread through the water, intermodulating, reinforcing or cancelling each other. The aggregate wave-front, by the time it reached human ears, was recognizable human speech.

'We are arrived, Shar and Lavon, according to the custom.'

'And welcome,' said Shar. 'Lavon, let's leave this matter of the plates for a while, until you hear what Para has to say; that's a part of the knowledge Lavons must have as they come of age, and it comes before the plates. I can give you some hints of what we are. First Para has to tell you something about what we aren't.'

Lavon nodded, willingly enough, and watched the proto as it settled gently to the surface of the hewn table at which Shar had been sitting. There was in the entity such a perfection and economy of organization, such a grace and surety of movement, that he could hardly believe in his own new-won maturity. Para, like all the protos, made him feel not, perhaps, poorly thought-out, but at least unfinished.

'We know that in this universe there is logically no place for man,' the gleaming, now immobile cylinder upon the table droned abruptly. 'Our memory is the common property to all our races. It reaches back to a time when there were no such creatures as men here. It remembers also that once upon a day there were men here, suddenly, and in some numbers. Their spores littered the bottom; we found the spores only a short time after our season's Awakening, and in them we saw the forms of men slumbering.

'Then men shattered their spores and emerged. They were intelligent, active. And they were gifted with a trait, a character, possessed by no other creature in this world. Not even the savage Eaters had it. Men organized us to exterminate the Eaters and therein lay the difference. Men had initiative. We have the word now, which you gave us, and we apply it, but we still do not know what the thing is that it labels.'

'You fought beside us,' Lavon said.

'Gladly. We would never have thought of that war by ourselves, but it was good and brought good. Yet we wondered. We saw that men were poor swimmers, poor walkers, poor crawlers, poor climbers. We saw that men were formed to make and use tools, a concept we still do not understand, for so wonderful a gift is largely wasted in this universe, and there is no other. What good are tool-useful members such as the hands of men? We do not know. It seems plain that so radical a thing should lead to a much greater rulership over the world than has, in fact, proven to be possible for men.'

Lavon's head was spinning. 'Para, I had no notion that you people were philosophers.'

'The protos are old,' Shar said. He had again turned to look out of the window, his hands locked behind his back. 'They aren't philosophers, Lavon, but they are remorseless logicians. Listen to Para.'

'To this reasoning there could be but one outcome,' the Para said. 'Our strange ally, Man, was like nothing else in this universe. He was and is ill-fitted for it. He does not belong here; he has been – adopted. This drives us to think that there are other universes besides this one, but where these universes might lie, and what their properties might be, it is impossible to imagine. We have no imagination, as men know.'

Was the creature being ironic? Lavon could not tell. He said slowly: 'Other universes? How could that be true?'

'We do not know,' the Para's uninflected voice hummed. Lavon waited, but obviously the proto had nothing more to say.

Shar had resumed sitting on the window sill, clasping his knees, watching the come and go of dim shapes in the lighted gulf. 'It is quite true,' he said. 'What is written on the remaining plates makes it plain. Let me tell you now what they say.

'*We were made*, Lavon. We were made by men who are not as we are, but men who were our ancestors all the same. They were caught in some disaster, and they made us, and put us here in our universe – so that, even though they had to die, the race of men would live.'

Lavon surged up from the woven spyrogyra mat upon which he had been sitting. 'You must think I'm a fool!' he said sharply.

'No. You're our Lavon; you have a right to know the facts. Make what you like of them.' Shar swung his webbed toes back into the chamber. 'What I've told you may be hard to believe, but it seems to be so; what Para says backs it up. Our unfitness to live here is self-evident. I'll give you some examples:

'The past four Shars discovered that we won't get any further in our studies until we learn how to control heat. We've produced enough heat chemically to show that even the water around us changes when the temperature gets high enough. But there we're stopped.'

'Why?'

'Because heat produced in open water is carried off as rapidly as it produced. Once we tried to enclose that heat, and we blew up a whole tube of the castle and killed everything in range; the shock was terrible. We measured the pressures that were involved in that explosion, and we discovered that no substance we know could have resisted them. Theory suggests some stronger substance – *but we need heat to form them*!

'Take our chemistry. We live in water. Everything seems to dissolve in water, to some extent. How do we confine a chemical test to the crucible we put it in? How do we maintain a solution at one dilution? I don't know. Every avenue leads me to the same stone door. We're thinking creatures, Lavon, but there's something drastically wrong in the way we think about this universe we live in. It just doesn't seem to lead to results.'

Lavon pushed back his floating hair futilely. 'Maybe

you're thinking about the wrong results. We've had no trouble with warfare, or crops, or practical things like that. If we can't create much heat, well, most of us won't miss it; we don't need any. What's the other universe supposed to be like, the one our ancestors lived in? Is it any better than this one?'

'I don't know,' Shar admitted. 'It was so different that it's hard to compare the two. The metal plates tell a story about men who were travelling from one place to another in a container that moved by itself. The only analogy I can think of is the shallops of diatom shells that our youngsters use to sled along the thermocline; but evidently what's meant is something much bigger.

'I picture a huge shallop, closed on all sides, big enough to hold many people – maybe twenty or thirty. It had to travel for generations through some kind of space where there wasn't any water to breathe, so that the people had to carry their own water and renew it constantly. There were no seasons; no yearly turnover; no ice forming on the sky, because there wasn't any sky in a closed shallop; no spore formation.

'Then the shallop was wrecked somehow. The people in it knew they were going to die. They made us, and put us here, as if we were their children. Because they had to die, they wrote their story on the plates, to tell us what happened. I suppose we'd understand it better if we had the plate Shar III lost during the war, but we don't.'

'The whole thing sounds like a parable,' Lavon said, shrugging. 'Or a song. I can see why you don't understand it. What I can't see is why you bother to try.'

'Because of the plates,' Shar said. 'You've handled them yourself, so you know that we've nothing like them. We have crude, impure metals we've hammered out, metals that last for a while and then decay. But the plates shine on and on, generation after generation. They don't change; our hammers and graving tools break against them; the little heat we can generate leaves them unharmed. Those plates weren't formed in our universe – and that one fact makes every word on them important to me. Someone went to a great deal of trouble to make those plates indestructible to give them to us. Someone to whom the word "stars" was important enough to be worth fourteen repetitions, despite the fact that the word doesn't seem to mean anything. I'm ready to think that if our makers repeated the word even twice on a record that seems likely to last forever, it's important for us to know what it means.'

'All these extra universes and huge shallops and meaningless words – I can't say that they don't exist, but I don't see what difference it makes. The Shars of a few generations ago spent their whole lives breeding better algae crops for us, and showing us how to cultivate them instead of living haphazardly off bacteria. That was work worth doing. The Lavons of those days evidently got along without the metal plates, and saw to it that the Shars did, too: well, as far as I'm concerned, you're welcome to the plates, if you like them better than crop improvement – but I think they ought to be thrown away.'

'All right,' Shar said, shrugging. 'If you don't want them, that ends the traditional interview. We'll go our—'

There was a rising drone from the table-top. The Para was lifting itself, waves of motion passing over its cilia, like the waves which went across the fruiting stalks of the fields of delicate fungi with which the bottom was planted. It had been so silent that Lavon had forgotten it; he could tell from Shar's startlement that Shar had, too.

'This is a great decision,' the waves of sound washing from the creature throbbed. 'Every proto has heard it and agrees with it. We have been afraid of these metal plates for a long time, afraid that men would learn to understand them and to follow what they say to some secret place, leaving the protos behind. Now we are not afraid.'

'There wasn't anything to be afraid of,' Lavon said indulgently.

'No Lavon before you had said so,' Para said. 'We are glad. We will throw the plates away.'

With that, the shining creature swooped towards the embrasure. With it, it bore away the remaining plates, which had been resting under it on the table-top, suspended delicately in the curved tips of its supple cilia. With a cry, Shar plunged through the water towards the opening.

'Stop, Para!'

But Para was already gone, so swiftly that he had not even heard the call. Shar twisted his body and brought up on one shoulder against the tower wall. He said nothing. His face was enough. Lavon could not look at it for more than an instant.

The shadows of the two men moved slowly along the uneven cobbled floor. The Noc descended towards them from the vault, its single thick tentacle stirring the water, its internal light flaring and fading irregularly. It, too, drifted through the window after its cousin, and sank slowly away towards the bottom. Gently its living glow dimmed, flickering, winked out.

II

For many days, Lavon was able to avoid thinking much about the loss. There was always a great deal of work to be done. Maintenance of the castles, which had been built by the now-extinct Eaters rather than by human hands, was a never-ending task. The thousand dichotomously branching wings tended to crumble, especially at their bases where they sprouted from each other, and no Shar had yet come forward with a mortar as good as the rotifer-spittle which had once held them together. In addition, the breaking through of windows and the construction of chambers in the early days had been haphazard and often unsound. The instinctive architecture of the rotifers, after all, had not been meant to meet the needs of human occupants.

And then there were the crops. Men no longer fed precariously upon passing bacteria; now there were the drifting mats of specific water-fungi, rich and nourishing, which had been bred by five generations of Shars. These had to be tended constantly to keep the strains pure, and to keep the older and less intelligent species of the protos from grazing on them. In this latter task, to be sure, the more intricate and far-seeing proto types cooperated, but men were needed to supervise.

There had been a time, after the war with the Eaters, when it had been customary to prey upon the slow-moving and stupid diatoms, whose exquisite and fragile glass shells were so easily burst, and who were unable to learn that a friendly voice did not necessarily means a friend. There were still people who would crack open a diatom when no one else was looking, but they were re-garded as barbarians, to the puzzlement of the protos.

The blurred and simple-minded speech of the gorgeously engraved plants had brought them into the category of pets – a concept which the protos were utterly unable to grasp, especially since men admitted that diatoms on the half-frustrule were delicious.

Lavon had had to agree, very early, that the distinction was tiny. After all, humans did eat the desmids, which differed from the diatoms only in three particulars: their shells were flexible, they could not move, and they did not speak. Yet to Lavon, as to most men, there did seem to be some kind of distinction, whether the protos could see it or not, and that was that. Under the circumstance he felt that it was a part of his duty, as a leader of men, to protect the diatoms from the occasional poachers who browsed upon them, in defiance of custom, in the high levels of the sunlit sky.

Yet Lavon found it impossible to keep himself busy enough to forget that moment when the last clues to Man's origin and destination had been seized and borne away into dim space.

It might be possible to ask Para for the return of the plates, explain that a mistake had been made. The protos were creatures of implacable logic, but they respected Man, were used to illogic in Man, and might reverse their decision if pressed—

We are sorry. The plates were carried over the bar and released in the gulf. We will have the bottom there searched, but . . .

With a sick feeling he could not repress, Lavon knew that when the protos decided something was worthless, they did not hide it in some chamber like old women. They threw it away – efficiently.

Yet despite the tormenting of his conscience, Lavon was convinced that the plates were well lost. What had they ever done for Man, except to provide Shars with useless things to think about in the late seasons of their lives? What the Shars themselves had done to benefit Man, here, in the water, in the world, in the universe, had been done by direct experimentation. No bit of useful knowledge ever had come from the plates. There had never been anything in the plates but things best left unthought. The protos were right.

Lavon shifted his position on the plant frond, where he had been sitting in order to overlook the harvesting of an experimental crop of blue-green, oil-rich algae drifting in a clotted mass close to the top of the sky, and scratched his back gently against the coarse bole. The protos were seldom wrong, after all. Their lack of creativity, their inability to think an original thought, was a gift as well as a limitation. It allowed them to see and feel things at all times as they were — not as they hoped they might be, for they had no ability to hope, either.

'La-von! Laa-vah-on!'

The long halloo came floating up from the sleepy depths. Propping one hand against the top of the frond, Lavon bent and looked down. One of the harvesters was looking up at him, holding loosely the adze with which he had been splitting free the glutinous tetrads of the algae.

'Up here. What's the matter?'

'We have the ripened quadrant cut free. Shall we tow it away?'

'Tow it away,' Lavon said, with a lazy gesture. He leaned back again. At the same instant, a brilliant reddish glory burst into being above him, and cast itself down towards the depths like mesh after mesh of the finest-drawn gold. The great light which lived above the sky during the day, brightening or dimming according to some pattern no Shar ever had fathomed, was blooming again.

Few men, caught in the warm glow of that light, could resist looking up at it — especially when the top of the sky itself wrinkled and smiled just a moment's climb or swim away. Yet, as always, Lavon's bemused upward look gave him back nothing but his own distorted, bobbling reflection, and a reflection of the plant on which he rested.

Here was the upper limit, the third of the three surfaces of the universe.

The first surface was the bottom, where the water ended.

The second surface was the thermocline, the invisible division between the colder waters of the bottom and the warm, light waters of the sky. During the height of the warm weather, the thermocline was so definite a division as to make for good sledding and for chilly passage. A real interface formed between the cold, denser, bottom waters and the warm reaches above, and maintained itself almost for the whole of the warm season.

The third surface was the sky. One could no more pass through that surface than one could penetrate the bottom, nor was there any better reason to try. There the universe ended. The light which played over it daily, waxing and waning as it chose, seemed to be one of its properties.

Towards the end of the season, the water gradually grew colder and more difficult to breathe, while at the same time the light became duller and stayed for shorter periods between darknesses. Slow currents started to move. The high waters turned chill and began to fall. The bottom mud stirred and smoked away, carrying with it the spores of the fields of fungi. The thermocline tossed, became choppy, and melted away. The sky began to fog with particles of soft silt carried up from the bottom, the walls, the corners of the universe. Before very long, the whole world was cold, inhospitable, flocculent with yellowing, dying creatures.

Then the protos encysted; the bacteria, even most of the plants and, not long afterwards, men, too, curled up in their oil-filled amber shells. The world died until the first tentative current of warm water broke the winter silence.

'La-von!'

Just after the long call, a shining bubble rose past Lavon. He reached out and poked it, but it bounded away from his sharp thumb. The gas-bubbles which rose from the bottom in late summer were almost invulnerable – and when some especially hard blow or edge did penetrate them, they broke into smaller bubbles which nothing could touch, and fled towards the sky, leaving behind a remarkably bad smell.

Gas. There was no water inside a bubble. A man who got inside a bubble would have nothing to breathe.

But, of course, it was impossible to penetrate a bubble. The surface tension was too strong. As strong as Shar's metal plates. As strong as the top of the sky.

As strong as the top of the sky. And above that – once the bubble was broken – a world of gas instead of water? Were all worlds bubbles of water drifting in gas?

If it were so, travel between them would be out of the question since it would be impossible to pierce the sky to begin with. Nor did the infant cosmology include any provisions for bottoms for the worlds.

And yet some of the local creatures did burrow *into* the bottom, quite deeply, seeking something in those depths which was beyond the reach of Man. Even the surface of the ooze, in high summer, crawled with tiny creatures for which mud was a natural medium. Man, too, passed freely between the two countries of water which were divided by the thermocline, though many of the creatures with which he lived could not pass that line at all, once it had established itself.

And if the new universe of which Shar had spoken existed at all, it had to exist beyond the sky, where the light was. Why could not the sky be passed, after all? The fact that bubbles could be broken showed that the surface skin that formed between water and gas wasn't completely invulnerable. Had it ever been tried?

Lavon did not suppose that one man could butt his way through the top of the sky, any more than he could burrow into the bottom, but there might be ways around the difficulty. Here at his back, for instance, was a plant which gave every appearance of continuing beyond the sky: its uppermost fronds broke off and were bent back only by a trick of reflection.

It had always been assumed that the plants died where they touched the sky. For the most part, they did, for frequently the dead extension could be seen, bleached and yellow, the boxes of its component cells empty, floating imbedded in the perfect mirror. But some were simply chopped off, like the one which sheltered him now. Perhaps that was only an illusion, and instead it soared indefinitely into some other place – some place where men might once have been born, and might still live . . .

The plates were gone. There was only one other way to find out.

Determinedly, Lavon began to climb towards the wavering mirror of the sky. His thorn-thumbed feet trampled obliviously upon the clustered sheaves of fragile stippled diatoms. The tulip-heads of Vortae, placid and murmurous cousins of Para, retracted startledly out of his way upon coiling stalks, to make silly gossip behind him.

Lavon did not hear them. He continued to climb doggedly towards the light, his fingers and toes gripping the plant-bole.

'Lavon! Where are you going? Lavon!'

He leaned out and looked down. The man with the adze, a doll-like figure, was beckoning to him from a patch of blue-green retracting over a violet abyss. Dizzily he looked away, clinging to the bole; he had never been so high before. Then he began to climb again.

After a while, he touched the sky with one hand. He stopped to breathe. Curious bacteria gathered about the base of his thumb where blood from a small cut was fogging away, scattered at his gesture, and wriggled mindlessly back towards the dull red lure.

He waited until he no longer felt winded, and resumed climbing. The sky pressed down against the top of his head, against the back of his neck, against his shoulders. It seemed to give slightly, with a tough, frictionless elasticity. The water here was intensely bright, and quite colourless. He climbed another step, driving his shoulders against that enormous weight.

It was fruitless. He might as well have tried to penetrate a cliff.

Again he had to rest. While he panted, he made a curious discovery. All around the bole of the water plant, the steel surface of the sky curved upward, making a kind of sheath. He found that he could insert his hand into it – there was almost enough space to admit his head as well. Clinging closely to the bole, he looked up into the inside of the sheath, probing with his injured hand. The glare was blinding.

There was a kind of soundless explosion. His whole wrist was suddenly encircled in an intense, impersonal grip, as if it were being cut in two. In blind astonishment, he lunged upward.

The ring of pain travelled smoothly down his upflung arm as he rose, was suddenly around his shoulders and chest. Another lunge and his knees were being squeezed in the circular vice. Another—

Something was horribly wrong. He clung to the bole and tried to gasp, but there was – nothing to breathe.

The water came streaming out of his body, from his mouth, his nostrils, the spiracles in his sides, spurting in tangible jets. An intense and fiery itching crawled over the entire surface of his body. At each spasm, long knives ran into him, and from a great distance he heard more water being expelled from his book-lungs in an obscene, frothy sputtering.

Lavon was drowning.

With a final convulsion, he kicked himself away from the splintery bole, and fell. A hard impact shook him; and then the water, which had clung to him so tightly when he had first attempted to leave it, took him back with cold violence.

Sprawling and tumbling grotesquely, he drifted, down and down and down, towards the bottom.

III

For many days, Lavon lay curled insensibly in his spore, as if in the winter sleep. The shock of cold which he had felt on re-entering his native universe had been taken by his body as a sign of coming winter, as it had taken the oxygen-starvation of his brief sojourn above the sky. The spore-forming glands had at once begun to function.

Had it not been for this, Lavon would surely have died. The danger of drowning disappeared even as he fell, as the air bubbled out of his lungs and re-admitted the life-giving water. But for acute desiccation and third degree sunburn, the sunken universe knew no remedy. The healing amnionic fluid generated by the spore-forming glands, after the transparent amber sphere had enclosed him, offered Lavon his only chance.

The brown sphere was spotted after some days by a prowling ameba, quiescent in the eternal winter of the bottom. Down there the temperature was always an even 4°, no matter what the season, but it was unheard of that a spore should be found there while the high epilimnion was still warm and rich in oxygen.

Within an hour, the spore was surrounded by scores of astonished protos, jostling each other to bump their blunt eyeless prows against the shell. Another hour later, a squad of worried men came plunging from the castles far above to press their own noses against the transparent wall. Then swift orders were given.

Four Paras grouped themselves about the amber sphere, and there was a subdued explosion as the trichocysts which lay imbedded at the bases of their cilia, just under the pellicle, burst and cast fine lines of a quickly solidifying liquid into the water. The four Paras thrummed and lifted, tugging.

Lavon's spore swayed gently in the mud and then rose slowly, entangled in the web. Nearby, a Noc cast a cold pulsating glow over the operation – not for the Paras, who did not need the light, but for the baffled knot of men. The sleeping figure of Lavon, head bowed, knees drawn up to its chest, revolved with an absurd solemnity inside the shell as it was moved.

'Take him to Shar, Para.'

The young Shar justified, by minding his own business, the traditional wisdom with which his hereditary office had invested him. He observed at once that there was nothing he could do for the encysted Lavon which would not be classified as simple meddling.

He had the sphere deposited in a high tower room of his castle, where there was plenty of light and the water was warm, which should suggest to the hibernating form that spring was again on the way. Beyond that, he simply sat and watched, and kept his speculations to himself.

Inside the spore, Lavon's body seemed rapidly to be shedding its skin, in long strips and patches. Gradually, his curious shrunkenness disappeared. His withered arms and legs and sunken abdomen filled out again.

The days went by while Shar watched. Finally he could discern no more changes, and, on a hunch, had the spore taken up to the topmost battlements of the tower, into the direct daylight.

An hour later, Lavon moved in his amber prison.

He uncurled and stretched, turning blank eyes up towards the light. His expression was that of a man who had not yet awakened from a ferocious nightmare. His whole body shone with a strange pink newness.

Shar knocked gently on the wall of the spore. Lavon turned his blind face towards the sound, life coming into his eyes. He smiled tentatively and braced his hands and feet against the inner wall of the shell.

The whole sphere fell abruptly to pieces with a sharp crackling. The amnionic fluid dissipated around him and Shar, carrying away with it the suggestive odour of a bitter struggle against death.

Lavon stood among the bits of shell and looked at Shar silently. At last he said:

'Shar – I've been beyond the sky.'

'I know,' Shar said gently.

Again Lavon was silent. Shar said, 'Don't be humble, Lavon. You've done an epoch-making thing. It nearly cost you your life. You must tell me the rest – all of it.'

'The rest?'

'You taught me a lot while you slept. Or are you still opposed to useless knowledge?'

Lavon could say nothing. He no longer could tell what he knew from what he wanted to know. He had only one question left, but he could not utter it. He could only look dumbly into Shar's delicate face.

'You have answered me,' Shar said, even more gently. 'Come my friend; join me at my table. We will plan our journey to the stars.'

It was two winter sleeps after Lavon's disastrous climb beyond the sky that all work on the spaceship stopped. By then, Lavon knew that he had hardened and weathered into that temporarily ageless state a man enters after he has just reached his prime; and he knew also that there were wrinkles engraved upon his brow, to stay and to deepen.

'Old' Shar, too, had changed, his features losing some of their delicacy as he came into his maturity. Though the wedge-shaped bony structure of his face would give him a withdrawn and poetic look for as long as he lived, participation in the plan had given his expression a kind of executive overlay, which at best gave it a mask-like rigidity, and at worst coarsened it somehow.

Yet despite the bleeding away of the years, the spaceship was still only a hulk. It lay upon a platform built above the tumbled boulders of the sandbar which stretched out from one wall of the world. It was an immense hull of pegged wood, broken by regularly spaced gaps through which the raw beams of the skeleton could be seen.

Work upon it had progressed fairly rapidly at first, for it was not hard to visualize what kind of vehicle would be needed to crawl through empty space without losing its water. It had been recognized that the sheer size of the machine would enforce a long period of construction, perhaps two full seasons, but neither Shar nor Lavon had anticipated any serious snag.

For that matter, part of the vehicle's apparent incompleteness was an illusion. About a third of its fittings were to consist of living creatures, which could not be expected to install themselves in the vessel much before the actual take-off.

Yet time and time again, work on the ship had had to be halted for long periods. Several times whole sections needed to be ripped out, as it became more and more evident that hardly a single normal, understandable concept could be applied to the problem of space travel.

The lack of the history plates, which the Para steadfastly refused to deliver up, was a double handicap. Immediately upon their loss, Shar had set himself to reproduce them from memory; but unlike the more religious of his people, he had never regarded them as holy writ, and hence had never set himself to memorizing them word by word. Even before the theft, he had accumulated a set of variant translations of passages presenting specific experimental problems, which were stored in his library, carved in wood. But most of these translations tended to contradict each other, and none of them related to spaceship construction, upon which the original had been vague in any case.

No duplicates of the cryptic characters of the original had ever been made, for the simple reason that there was nothing in the sunken universe capable of destroying the originals, nor of duplicating their apparently changeless permanence. Shar remarked too late that through simple caution they should have made a number of verbatim temporary records – but after generations of green-gold peace, simple caution no longer covers preparation against catastrophe. (Nor, for that matter, did a culture which had to dig each letter of its simple alphabet into pulpy waterlogged wood with a flake of stonewort, encourage the keeping of records in triplicate.)

As a result, Shar's imperfect memory of the contents of the history plates, plus the constant and millennial doubt as to the accuracy of the various translations, proved finally to be the worst obstacle to progress on the spaceship itself.

'Men must paddle before they can swim,' Lavon observed belatedly, and Shar was forced to agree with him.

Obviously, whatever the ancients had known about

spaceship construction, very little of that knowledge was usable to a people still trying to build its first spaceship from scratch. In retrospect, it was not surprising that the great hulk still rested incomplete upon its platform above the sand boulders, exuding a musty odour of wood steadily losing its strength, two generations after its flat bottom had been laid down.

The fat-faced young man who headed the strike delegation was Phil XX, a man two generations younger than Lavon, four younger than Shar. There were crow's-feet at the corners of his eyes, which made him look both like a querulous old man and like an infant spoiled in the spore.

'We're calling a halt to this crazy project,' he said bluntly. 'We've slaved our youth away on it, but now that we're our own masters, it's over, that's all. Over.'

'Nobody's compelled you,' Lavon said angrily.

'Society does; our parents do,' a gaunt member of the delegation said. 'But now we're going to start living in the real world. Everybody these days knows that there's no other world but this one. You oldsters can hang on to your superstitions if you like. We don't intend to.'

Baffled, Lavon looked over at Shar. The scientist smiled and said, 'Let them go, Lavon. We have no use for the faint-hearted.'

The fat-faced young man flushed. 'You can't insult us into going back to work. We're through. Build your own ship to no place!'

'All right,' Lavon said evenly. 'Go on, beat it. Don't stand around here orating about it. You've made your decision and we're not interested in your self-justifications. Good-bye.'

The fat-faced young man evidently still had quite a bit of heroism to dramatize which Lavon's dismissal had short-circuited. An examination of Lavon's stony face, however, convinced him that he had to take his victory as he found it. He and the delegation trailed ingloriously out of the archway.

'Now what?' Lavon asked when they had gone. 'I must admit Shar, that I would have tried to persuade them. We do need the workers, after all.'

'Not as much as they need us,' Shar said tranquilly. 'How many volunteers have you got for the crew of the ship?'

'Hundreds. Every young man of the generation after Phil's wants to go along. Phil's wrong about that segment of the population, at least. The project catches the imagination of the very young.'

'Did you give them any encouragement?'

'Sure,' Lavon said. 'I told them we'd call on them if they were chosen. But you can't take that seriously! We'd do badly to displace our picked group of specialists with youths who have enthusiasm and nothing else.'

'That's not what I had in mind, Lavon. Didn't I see a Noc in your chambers somewhere? Oh, there he is, asleep in the dome. Noc!'

The creature stirred its tentacles lazily.

'Will you give us back the plates?'

'No, Lavon. We have never denied you anything before, but this we must.'

'You're going with us though, Para. Unless you give us the knowledge we need, you'll lose your life if we lose ours.'

'What is one Para?' the creature said. 'We are all alike. This cell will die; but the protos need to know how you fare on this journey. We believe you should make it without the plates.'

'Why?'

The proto was silent. Lavon stared at it a moment, then turned deliberately back to the speaking tubes.

'Noc, I've a message,' Shar called. 'The protos are to tell all men that those who wish to go to the next world with the spaceship must come to the staging area right away. Say that we can't promise to take everyone, but that only those who help us build the ship will be considered at all.'

The Noc curled its tentacles again and appeared to go back to sleep. Actually of course, it was sending its message through the water in all directions.

IV

Lavon turned from the arrangement of speaking-tube megaphones which was his control board and looked at the Para. 'One last try,' he said. 'Everyone hang on,' he said. He felt shaky. 'We're about to start. Tarol, is the ship sealed?'

'As far as I can tell, Lavon.'

Lavon shifted to another megaphone. He took a deep breath. Already the water seemed stifling, though the ship hadn't moved.

'Ready with one-quarter power. One, two, three, *go*.'

The whole ship jerked and settled back into place again. The raphe diatoms along the under hull settled into their niches, their jelly treads turning against broad endless belts of crude leather. Wooden gears creaked, stepping up the slow power of the creatures, transmitting it to the sixteen axles of the ship's wheels.

The ship rocked and began to roll slowly along the sandbar. Lavon looked tensely through the mica port. The world flowed painfully past him, he could feel the electric silence of Shar, Para, the two alternate pilots, as if their gaze were stabbing directly through his body and on out of the port. The world looked different, now that he was leaving it. How had he missed all this beauty before?

The slapping of the endless belts and the squeaking and groaning of the gears and axles grew louder as the slope steepened. The ship continued to climb, lurching. Around it, squadrons of men and protos dipped and wheeled, escorting it towards the sky.

Gradually the sky lowered and pressed down towards the top of the ship.

'A little more work from your diatoms, Tanol,' Lavon said. 'Boulder ahead.' The ship swung ponderously. 'All right, slow them up again. Give us a shove from your side, Than – no, that's too much – there, that's it. Back to normal; you're still turning us! Tanol, give us one burst to line us up again. Good. All right, steady drive on all sides. Won't be long now.'

'How can you think in webs like that?' the Para wondered behind him.

'I just do, that's all. It's the way men think. Overseers, a little more thrust now; the grade's getting steeper.'

The gears groaned. The ship nosed up. The sky brightened in Lavon's face. Despite himself, he began to be frightened. His lungs seemed to burn, and in his mind he felt his long fall through nothingness towards the chill slap of water as if he were experiencing it for the first time. His skin itched and burned. Could he go up *there* again? Up there into the burning void, the great gasping agony where no life should go?

The sandbar began to level out and the going became a little easier. Up here, the sky was so close that the lumbering motion of the huge ship disturbed it. Shadows of wavelets ran across the sand. Silently, the thick-barrelled bands of blue-green algae drank in the light and converted it to oxygen, writhing in their slow mindless dance just under the long mica skylight which ran along the spine of the ship. In the hold, beneath the latticed corridor and cabin floors, whirring Vortae kept the ship's water in motion, fuelling themselves upon drifting organic particles.

One by one, the figures wheeling about the ship outside waved arms or cilia and fell back, coasting down the slope of the sand-bar towards the familiar world, dwindling and disappearing. There was at last only one single Euglena, half-plant cousin of the protos, forging along beside the spaceship into the marches of the shallows. It loved the light, but finally it, too, was driven away into cooler, deeper waters, its single whip-like tentacle undulating placidly as it went. It was not very bright, but Lavon felt deserted when it left.

Where they were going, though, none could follow.

Now the sky was nothing but a thin, resistant skin of water coating the top of the ship. The vessel slowed, and when Lavon called for more power, it began to dig itself in among the sandgrains.

'That's not going to work,' Shar said tensely. 'I think we'd better step down the gear ratio, Lavon, so you can apply stress more slowly.'

'All right,' Lavon agreed. 'Full stop, everybody. Shar, will you supervise gear-changing, please?'

Insane brilliance of empty space looked Lavon full in the face just beyond his big mica bull's-eye. It was maddening to be forced to stop here upon the threshold of infinity; and it was dangerous, too. Lavon could feel building in him the cold fear of the outside. A few moments more of inaction, he knew with a gathering coldness at the pit of his stomach, and he would be unable to go through with it.

Surely, he thought, there must be a better way to change gear ratios than the traditional one, which involved dismantling almost the entire gear-box. Why couldn't a number of gears of different sizes be carried on the same shaft, not necessarily all in action all at once, but awaiting use simply by shoving the axle back and forth longitudinally in its sockets? It would still be clumsy, but it could be worked on orders from the bridge and would not involve shutting down the entire machine – and throwing the new pilot into a blue-green funk.

Shar came lunging up through the trap and swam himself to a stop.

'All set,' he said. 'The big reduction gears aren't taking the strain too well, though.'

'Splintering?'

'Yes. I'd go it slow at first.'

Lavon nodded mutely. Without allowing himself to stop, even for a moment, to consider the consequences of his words, he called: 'Half power.'

The ship hunched itself down again and began to move, very slowly indeed, but more smoothly than before. Overhead, the sky thinned to complete transparency. The great light came blasting in. Behind Lavon there was an uneasy stir. The whiteness grew at the front ports.

Again the ship slowed, straining against the blinding barrier. Lavon swallowed and called for more power. The ship groaned like something about to die. It was now almost at a standstill.

'More power,' Lavon ground out.

Once more, with infinite slowness, the ship began to move. Gently, it tilted upward.

Then it lunged forward and every board and beam in it began to squall.

'Lavon! Lavon!'

Lavon started sharply at the shout. The voice was coming at him from one of the megaphones, the one marked for the port at the rear of the ship.

'Lavon!'

'What is it? Stop your damn yelling.'

'I can see the top of the sky! From the *other* side, from the top side! It's like a big flat sheet of metal. We're going away from it. We're above the sky, Lavon, we're above the sky!'

Another violent start swung Lavon around towards the forward port. On the outside of the mica, the water was evaporating with shocking swiftness, taking with it strange distortions and patterns made of rainbows.

Lavon saw space.

It was at first like a deserted and cruelly dry version of the bottom. There were enormous boulders, great cliffs, tumbled, split, riven, jagged rocks going up and away in all directions.

But it had a sky of its own – a deep blue dome so far away that he could not believe in, let alone compute, what its distance might be. And in this dome was a ball of white fire that seared his eyeballs.

The wilderness of rock was still a long way away from the ship, which now seemed to be resting upon a level, glistening plain. Beneath the surface-shine, the plain seemed to be made of sand, nothing but familiar sand, the same substance which had heaped up to form a bar in Lavon's own universe, the bar along which the ship had climbed. But the glassy, colourful skin over it—

Suddenly Lavon became conscious of another shout from the megaphone banks. He shook his head savagely and asked, 'What is it now?'

'Lavon, this is Than. What have you got us into? The belts are locked. The diatoms can't move them. They aren't faking either; we've rapped them hard enough to make them think we were trying to break their shells, but they still can't give us more power.'

'Leave them alone,' Lavon snapped. 'They can't fake; they haven't enough intelligence. If they say they can't give you more power, they can't.'

'Well, then, you get us out of it,' Than's voice said frightenedly.

Shar came forward to Lavon's elbow. 'We're on a space-water interface, where the surface tension is very high,' he said softly. 'This is why I insisted on our building the ship so that we could lift the wheels off the ground whenever necessary. For a long while I couldn't understand the reference of the history plates to "retractable landing gear", but it finally occurred to me that the tension along a space-water interface – or, to be more exact, a space-mud interface – would hold any large object pretty tightly. If you order the wheels pulled up now, I think we'll make better progress for a while on the belly-treads.'

'Good enough,' Lavon said. 'Hello below – up landing gear. Evidently the ancients knew their business after all, Shar.'

Quite a few minutes later, for shifting power to the belly-treads involved another setting of the gear-box, the ship was crawling along the shore towards the tumbled rock. Anxiously, Lavon scanned the jagged, threatening wall for a break. There was a sort of rivulet off towards the left which might offer a route, though a dubious one, to the next world. After some thought, Lavon ordered his ship turned towards it.

'Do you suppose that thing in the sky is a "star"? he asked. 'But there were supposed to be lots of them. Only one is up there – and one's plenty for *my* taste.'

'I don't know,' Shar admitted. 'But I'm beginning to get a picture of the way the universe is made, I think. Evidently our world is a sort of cup in the bottom of this huge one. This one has a sky of its own; perhaps it, too, is only a cup in the bottom of a still huger world, and so on and on without end. It's a hard concept to grasp, I'll admit. Maybe it would be more sensible to assume that all the worlds are cups in this one common surface, and that the great light shines on them all impartially.'

'Then what makes it seem to go out every night, and dim in the day during winter?' Lavon demanded.

'Perhaps it travels in circles, over first one world, then another. How could I know yet?'

'Well, if you're right, it means that all we have to do is crawl along here for a while, until we hit the top of the sky of another world,' Lavon said. 'Then we dive in. Somehow it seems too simple, after all our preparations.'

Shar chuckled, but the sound did not suggest that he had discovered anything funny. 'Simple? Have you noticed the temperature yet?'

Lavon had noticed it, just beneath the surface of awareness, but at Shar's remark he realized that he was gradually being stifled. The oxygen content of the water, luckily, had not dropped, but the temperature suggested the shallows in the last and worst part of the autumn. It was like trying to breathe soup.

'Than, give us more action from the Vortae,' Laven called. 'This is going to be unbearable unless we get more circulation.'

It was all he could do now to keep his attention on the business of steering the ship.

The cut or defile in the scattered razor-edged rocks was a little closer, but there still seemed to be many miles of rough desert to cross. After a while, the ship settled into a steady, painfully slow crawling, with less pitching and jerking than before, but also with less progress. Under it, there was now a sliding, grinding sound, rasping against the hull of the ship itself, as if it were treadmilling over some coarse lubricant whose particles were each as big as a man's head.

Finally Shar said, 'Lavon, we'll have to stop again. The sand this far up is dry, and we're wasting energy using the treads.'

'Are you sure we can take it?' Lavon asked, gasping for breath. 'At least we are moving. If we stop to lower the wheels and change gears again, we'll boil.'

'We'll boil if we don't,' Shar said calmly. 'Some of our algae are already dead and the rest are withering. That's a pretty good sign that we can't take much more. I don't think we'll make it into the shadows, unless we do change over and put on some speed.'

There was a gulping sound from one of the mechanics. 'We ought to turn back,' he said raggedly. 'We were never meant to be out here in the first place. We were made for the water, not this hell.'

'We'll stop,' Lavon said, 'but we're not turning back. That's final.'

The words made a brave sound, but the man had upset Lavon more than he dared to admit, even to himself. 'Shar,' he said, 'make it fast, will you?'

The scientist nodded and dived below.

The minutes stretched out. The great white globe in the sky blazed and blazed. It had moved down the sky, far down, so that the light was pouring into the ship directly in Lavon's face, illuminating every floating particle, its rays like long milky streamers. The currents of water passing Lavon's cheek were almost hot.

How could they dare go directly forward into that inferno? The land directly under the 'star' must be even hotter than it was here.

'Lavon! Look at Para!'

Lavon forced himself to turn and look at his proto ally. The great slipper had settled to the deck, where it was lying with only a feeble pulsation of its cilia. Inside, its vacuoles were beginning to swell, to become bloated, pear-shaped bubbles, crowding the granulated protoplasm, pressing upon the dark nuclei.

'This cell is dying,' Para said, as coldly as always. 'But go on – go on. There is much to learn, and you may live, even though we do not. Go on.'

'You're . . . for us now?' Lavon whispered.

'We have always been for you. Push your folly to its uttermost. We will benefit in the end, and so will Man.'

The whisper died away. Lavon called the creature again, but it did not respond.

There was a wooden clashing from below, and then Shar's voice came tinnily from one of the megaphones. 'Lavon, go ahead! The diatoms are dying, too, and then we'll be without power. Make it as quickly and directly as you can.'

Grimly, Lavon leaned forward. The 'star' is directly over the land we're approaching.'

'It is? It may go lower still and the shadows will get longer. That's our only hope.'

Lavon had not thought of that. He rasped into the banked megaphones. Once more, the ship began to move.

It got hotter.

Steadily, with a perceptible motion, the 'star' sank in Lavon's face. Suddenly a new terror struck him. Suppose it should continue to go down until it was gone entirely? Blasting though it was now, it was the only source of heat. Would not space become bitter cold on the instant – and the ship an expanding, bursting block of ice?

The shadows lengthened menacingly, stretched across the desert towards the forward-rolling vessel. There was no talking in the cabin, just the sound of ragged breathing and the creaking of the machinery.

Then the jagged horizon seemed to rush upon them. Stony teeth cut into the lower rim of the ball of fire, devoured it swiftly. It was gone.

They were in the lee of the cliffs. Lavon ordered the ship turned to parallel the rock-line; it responded heavily, sluggishly. Far above, the sky deepened steadily, from blue to indigo.

Shar came silently up through the trap and stood beside Lavon, studying that deepening colour and the lengthening of the shadows down the beach towards their world. He said nothing, but Lavon knew that the same chilling thought was in his mind.

'Lavon.'

Lavon jumped. Shar's voice had iron in it. 'Yes?'

'We'll have to keep moving. We must make the next world, wherever it is, very shortly.'

'How can we dare move when we can't see where we're going? Why not sleep it over — if the cold will let us?'

'It will let us,' Shar said. 'It can't get dangerously cold up here. If it did, the sky — or what we used to think of as the sky — would have frozen over every night, even in summer. But what I'm thinking about is the water. The plants will go to sleep now. In our world that wouldn't matter; the supply of oxygen is enough to last through the night. But in this confined space, with so many creatures in it and no source of fresh water, we will probably smother.'

Shar seemed hardly to be involved at all, but spoke rather with the voice of implacable physical laws.

'Furthermore,' he said, staring unseeingly out at the raw landscape, 'the diatoms are plants, too. In other words, we must stay on the move for as long as we have oxygen and power — and pray that we make it.'

'Shar, we had quite a few protos on board this ship once. And Para there isn't quite dead yet. If he were, the cabin would be intolerable. The ship is nearly sterile of bacteria, because all the protos have been eating them as a matter of course and there's no outside supply of them, any more than there is for oxygen. But still and all there would have been some decay.'

Shar bent and tested the pellicle of the motionless Para with a probing finger. 'You're right, he's still alive. What does that prove?'

'The Vortae are also alive; I can feel the water circulating. Which proves it wasn't the heat that hurt Para. *It was the light.* Remember how badly my skin was affected after I climbed beyond the sky? Undiluted starlight is deadly. We should add that to the information on the plates.'

'I still don't see the point.'

'It's this. We've got three or four Noc down below. They were shielded from the light, and so must be alive. If we concentrate them in the diatom galleys, the dumb diatoms will think it's still daylight and will go on working. Or we can concentrate them up along the spine of the ship, and keep the algae putting out oxygen. So the question is: which do we need more, oxygen or power? Or can we split the difference?'

Shar actually grinned. 'A brilliant piece of thinking. We'll make a Shar of you yet, Lavon. No, I'd say that we can't split the difference. There's something about daylight, some quality, that the light Noc emits doesn't have. You and I can't detect it, but the green plants can, and without it they don't make oxygen. So we'll have to settle for the diatoms – for power.'

Lavon brought the vessel away from the rocky lee of the cliff, out on to the smoother sand. All trace of direct light was gone now, although there was still a soft, general glow on the sky.

'Now, then,' Shar said thoughtfully, 'I would guess that there's water over there in the canyon, if we can reach it. I'll go below and arrange—'

Lavon gasped. 'What's the matter?'

Silently, Lavon pointed, his heart pounding.

The entire dome of indigo above them was spangled with tiny, incredibly brilliant lights. There were hundreds of them, and more and more were becoming visible as the darkness deepened. And far away, over the ultimate edge of the rocks, was a dim red globe, crescented with ghostly silver. Near the zenith was another such body, much smaller, and silvered all over . . .

Under the two moons of Hydrot, and under the eternal stars, the two-inch wooden spaceship and its microscopic cargo toiled down the slope towards the drying little rivulet.

V

The ship rested on the bottom of the canyon for the rest of the night. The great square doors were thrown open to admit the raw, irradiated, life-giving water from outside – and the wriggling bacteria which were fresh food.

No other creatures approached them, either with curiosity or with predatory intent, while they slept, though Lavon had posted guards at the doors. Evidently, even up here on the very floor of space, highly organized creatures were quiescent at night.

But when the first flush of light filtered through the water, trouble threatened.

First of all, there was the bug-eyed monster. The thing was green and had two snapping claws, either one of which could have broken the ship in two like a spyro-gyra straw. Its eyes were black and globular, on the ends of short columns, and its long feelers were as thick as a plant-bole. It passed in a kicking fury of motion, however, never noticing the ship at all.

'Is that – a sample of the kind of life we can expect in the next world?' Lavon whispered. Nobody answered, for the very good reason that nobody knew.

After a while, Lavon risked moving the ship forward against the current ,which was slow but heavy. Enormous writhing worms whipped past them. One struck the hull a heavy blow, then thrashed on obliviously.

'They don't notice us,' Shar said. 'We're too small. Lavon, the ancients warned us of the immensity of space, but even when you see it, it's impossible to grasp. And all those stars – can they mean what I think they mean? It's beyond thought, beyond belief!'

'The bottom's sloping,' Lavon said, looking ahead intently. 'The walls of the canyon are retreating, and the water's becoming rather silty. Let the stars wait, Shar; we're coming towards the entrance of our new world.'

Shar subsided moodily. His vision of space had disturbed him, perhaps seriously. He took little notice of the great thing that was happening, but instead huddled worriedly over his own expanding speculations. Lavon felt the old gap between their two minds widening once more.

Now the bottom was tilting upward again. Lavon had no experience with delta-formation, for no rivulets left his own world, and the phenomenon worried him. But his worries were swept away in wonder as the ship topped the rise and nosed over.

Ahead, the bottom sloped away again, indefinitely, into glimmering depths. A proper sky was over them once more, and Lavon could see small rafts of plankton floating placidly beneath it. Almost at once, too, he saw several of the smaller kinds of protos, a few of which were already approaching the ship—

Then the girl came darting out of the depths, her features distorted with terror. At first she did not see the ship at all. She came twisting and turning lithely through the water, obviously hoping only to throw herself over the ridge of the delta and into the savage streamlet beyond.

Lavon was stunned. Not that there were men here — he had hoped for that — but the girl's single-minded flight towards suicide.

'What—

Then a dim buzzing began to grow in his ears, and he understood.

'Shar! Than! Tanol!' he bawled. 'Break out crossbows and spears! Knock out all the windows!' He lifted a foot and kicked through the big port in front of him. Someone thrust a crossbow into his hand.

'Eh? What's happening?' Shar blurted.

'*Rotifers!*'

The cry went through the ship like a galvanic shock. The rotifers back in Lavon's own world were virtually extinct, but everyone knew thoroughly the grim history of the long battle Man and proto had waged against them.

The girl spotted the ship suddenly and paused, stricken by despair at the sight of the new monster. She drifted with her own momentum, her eyes alternately fixed hypnotically upon the ship and glancing back over her shoulder, towards where the buzzing snarled louder and louder in the dimness.

'Don't stop!' Lavon shouted. 'This way, this way! We're friends! We'll help!'

Three great semi-transparent trumpets of smooth flesh bored over the rise, the thick cilia of their coronas whirring greedily. Dicrans — the most predacious of the entire tribe of Eaters. They were quarrelling thickly among themselves as they moved, with the few blurred, pre-symbolic noises which made up their 'language'.

Carefully, Lavon wound the crossbow, brought it to his shoulder, and fired. The bolt sang away through the water. It lost momentum rapidly, and was caught by a stray current which brought it closer to the girl than to the Eater at which Lavon had aimed.

He bit his lip, lowered the weapon, wound it up again. It did not pay to underestimate the range; he would have to wait until he could fire with effect. Another bolt, cutting through the water from a side port, made him issue orders to cease firing.

The sudden irruption of the rotifers decided the girl.

The motionless wooden monster was strange to her and had not yet menaced her – but she must have known what it would be like to have three Dicrans over her, each trying to grab away from the other the biggest share. She threw herself towards the big port. The Eaters screamed with fury and greed and bored after her.

She probably would not have made it, had not the dull vision of the lead Dicran made out the wooden shape of the ship at the last instant. It backed off, buzzing, and the other two sheered away to avoid colliding with it. After that they had another argument, though they could hardly have formulated what it was that they were fighting about. They were incapable of saying anything much more complicated than the equivalent of 'Yaah', 'Drop dead', and 'You're another'.

While they were still snarling at each other, Lavon pierced the nearest one all the way through with an arablast bolt. It disintegrated promptly – rotifers are delicately organized creatures despite their ferocity – and the remaining two were at once involved in a lethal battle over the remains.

'Than, take a party out and spear me those two Eaters while they're still fighting,' Lavon ordered. 'Don't forget to destroy their eggs, too. I can see that this world needs a little taming.'

The girl shot through the port and brought up against the far wall of the cabin, flailing in terror. Lavon tried to approach her, but from somewhere she produced a flake of stonewort chipped to a nasty point. He sat down on the stool before his control board and waited while she took in the cabin, Lavon, Shar, the pilot, the senescent Para.

At last she said: 'Are – you – the gods from beyond the sky?'

'We're from beyond the sky, all right,' Lavon said. 'But we're not gods. We're human beings, like yourself. Are there many humans here?'

The girl seemed to assess the situation very rapidly, savage though she was. Lavon had the odd and impossible impression that he should recognize her. She tucked the knife back into her matted hair – ah, Lavon thought, that's a trick I may need to remember – and shook her head.

'We are few. The Eaters are everywhere. Soon they will have the last of us.'

Her fatalism was so complete that she actually did not seem to care.

'And you've never cooperated against them? Or asked the protos to help?'

'The protos?' She shrugged. 'They are as helpless as we are against the Eaters. We have no weapons which kill at a distance like yours. And it is too late now for such weapons to do any good. We are too few, the Eaters too many.'

Lavon shook his head emphatically. 'You've had one weapon that counts, all along. Against it, numbers mean nothing. We'll show you how we've used it. You may be able to use it even better than we did, once you've given it a try.'

The girl shrugged again. 'We have dreamed of such a weapon now and then, but never found it. I do not think that what you say is true. What is this weapon?'

'Brains,' Lavon said. 'Not just one brain, but brains. Working together. Cooperation.'

'Lavon speaks the truth,' a weak voice said from the deck.

The Para stirred feebly. The girl watched it with wide eyes. The sound of the Para using human speech seemed to impress her more than the ship or anything else it contained.'

'The Eaters can be conquered,' the thin, buzzing voice said. 'The protos will help, as they helped in the world from which we came. They fought this flight through space, and deprived Man of his records; but Man made the trip without the records. The protos will never oppose men again. I have already spoken to the protos of this world and have told them what Man can dream, Man can do, whether the protos wish it or not.

'Shar, your metal records are with you. They were hidden in the ship. My brothers will lead you to them.

'This organism dies now. It dies in confidence of knowledge, as an intelligent creature dies. Man has taught us this. There is nothing that knowledge . . . cannot do. With it, men . . . have crossed . . . have crossed space . . .'

The voice whispered away. The shining slipper did not change, but something about it was gone. Lavon looked at the girl; their eyes met.

'We have crossed space,' Lavon repeated softly.

Shar's voice came to him across a great distance. The young-old man was whispering: 'But *have* we?'

'As far as I'm concerned, yes,' said Lavon.

SURFACE TENSION

A common type of science fiction plot is that which deals with men the size of microorganisms, or the size of atoms. The basic assumption is that men can somehow be shrunk to tiny size yet remain men.

But how could this be done? Is the tiny man made up of fewer atoms, or are the atoms themselves miniaturized? If the atoms themselves are miniaturized, how could men live on food containing unminiaturized atoms, make use of unminiaturized oxygen to breathe? If the miniature man is made up of fewer atoms, are there sufficient atoms to keep him as complex as he is now; to give him a brain sufficiently complex to be intelligent?

I think we can safely say that by today's understanding of science the miniaturization of human beings, while keeping them alive and intelligent, is quite impossible.

Nevertheless, James Blish has a thorough understanding of science and it can be assumed that he is aware of the impossibility of his basic assumption. Why, then, did he do it?

Well, by doing so, he was able to give a fascinating picture of a world in which the plants and animals surrounding man were microorganisms. He could also describe the difficulties and heroism involved in the conquest of space, in terms of a tiny wooden vessel, making its way from one puddle to another.

Notice, too, that, having made his one basic impossible assumption, he does everything he can to make all else plausible. (It is sometimes said that a good science fiction writer makes one assumption – even if an impossible one – to start his story and then, no more.)

Questions and Suggestions

1. Blish makes use of microorganisms to substitute for machine technology. Noc supplies illumination, the Vortae supply water circulation and so on. Find information on the microorganisms called 'noctiluca' and 'vor-

189

ticella' and see if this sounds reasonable. What are the rotifera (the 'Eaters' of the story)? How would they seem to one-celled animals?

2. The most intelligent of the micro-organisms is Para. Check the description with that of the 'paramecium'. Notice that Para talks by the careful manipulation of its cilia. How do the cilia of the paramecium work and do you think that Para's ciliar manipulation is possible? Do you think it is possible for any organism at the level of complexity of the paramecium to be intelligent? Blish implies that there is a bond of union between all the Paras; that there is a multi-cellular organism built up of them although the individual cells are not in contact. Do you think that men might evolve in the direction of a multi-organismic creature, with each man being part of a total society with a superconsciousness? How might such a living society conduct itself? Would you like to be part of it?

3. Blish places the planet Hydrot (why the name?) in the Tau Ceti system. Tau Ceti is a real star. Where is it located and why does it have that name? What else can you find out about it? Why did Blish choose this star rather than Sirius, Rigel, or any of the other bright, familiar ones?

4. What is surface tension and why was it so difficult for the microscopic men to get out of the water and into the air? Does surface tension exist in our world and if it does, why are we not bothered by it? What other facts of the environment might bother a miniature man but does not bother us? What facts of the environment which are a greater danger to ourselves would not bother a miniature man?

APPENDIX

Further Reading

1. A MARTIAN ODYSSEY by Stanley G. Weinbaum
   Is There Life on Other Worlds? by Paul Anderson (Macmillan, 1963)
   We Are Not Alone by Walter Sullivan (Hodder, 1965)

2. NIGHT by Don A. Stuart
   Frontiers of Astronomy by Fred Hoyle (Heinemann, 1955)
   Great Ideas and Theories of Modern Cosmology by Jagjit Singh (Constable, 1963)

3. THE DAY IS DONE by Lester del Rey
   Mankind in the Making by William Howells (Secker and Warburg, 1961)
   Man, Time & Fossils by Ruth Moore (Jonathan Cape, 1962)

4. HEAVY PLANET by Lee Gregor
   Weather on the Planets by George Ohring (Doubleday, 1966)
   Earth, Moon, and Planets by Fred L. Whipple (Oxford University Press, 1968)

5. '—AND HE BUILT A CROOKED HOUSE—' by Robert A. Heinlein
   A New Look at Geometry by Irving Adler (Dobson, 1967)
   Introduction to Geometry by H. S. M. Coxeter (2nd ed., Wiley, 1969)

6. PROOF by Hal Clement
   The Sun by Giorgio Abetti (Faber and Faber, 1957)
   The Stars by W. Kruse and W. Dieckvoss (Mayflower, 1960)

7. A SUBWAY NAMED MOBIUS by A. J. Deutsch
   Intuitive Concepts in Elementary Topology by B. H. Arnold (Prentice-Hall, 1962)
   Experiments in Topology by Stephen Barr (John Murray, 1965)

8. SURFACE TENSION by James Blish
   Cells and Cell Structure by E. H. Mercer (Hutchinson Educational, 1961)

The Procession of Life by Alfred S. Romer (Weidenfeld and Nicolson, 1968)

9. COUNTRY DOCTOR by William Morrison
   Life on the Planets by Robert Tocquet (Grove, 1962)
   Life in the Universe by Michael W. Ovenden (Heinemann, 1964)

10. THE HOLES AROUND MARS by Jerome Bixby
    Celestial Mechanics by Y. Riabov (Dover, 1961)
    Astronautics for Science Teachers by John G. Meitner (Wiley, 1965)

11. THE DEEP RANGE by Arthur C. Clarke
    The Sea by Leonard Engel (Time, Inc., 1961)
    Whales by E. J. Slijper (Hutchinson, 1962)

12. THE CAVE OF NIGHT by James E. Gunn
    Appointment on the Moon by Richard S. Lewis (Viking, 1968) (revised edition, Ballantine, 1969)
    We Reach the Moon by John Noble Wilford (Bantam, 1969)

13. DUST RAG by Hal Clement
    Pictorial Guide to the Moon by Dinsmore Alter (Thomas Y. Crowell, 1967)
    The Case for Going to the Moon by Neil P. Ruzic (Putnam, 1965)

14. PÂTÉ DE FOIE GRAS by Isaac Asimov
    Isotopic Tracers in Biology by Martin David Kamen (3rd ed., Academic Press, 1957)
    Isotopes by J. L. Putnam (Pelican, 1960)

15. OMNILINGUAL by H. Beam Piper
    Lost Worlds by Leonard Cottrell (Elek Books, 1964)
    To the Rock of Darius: The Story of Henry Rawlinson by Robert Silverberg (Holt, Rinehart and Winston, 1966)

16. THE BIG BOUNCE by Walter S. Tevis
    The Laws of Physics by Milton A. Rothman (Basic Books, 1963)
    Understanding Physics by Isaac Asimov (Volume I, Allen and Unwin, 1967)

17. NEUTRON STAR by Larry Niven
    The Tides by Edward P. Clancy (McCorquodale, 1968)
    The Astounding Pulsars, Science Year, 1969, page 37 (Field Enterprises, 1969)